It's another Quality Book from CGP

This book is for anyone doing GCSE Double Science at Foundation Level.

It contains lots of tricky questions designed
to make you sweat — because that's the only
way you'll get any better.

It's also got some daft bits in to try and make
the whole experience at least vaguely
entertaining for you.

What CGP is all about

Our sole aim here at CGP is to produce the highest quality
books — carefully written, immaculately presented and
dangerously close to being funny.

Then we work our socks off to get them out to you
— at the cheapest possible prices.

Contents

Section Four — Human Biology Part Two

Section Five — Genetics and Evolution

Section Six — The Environment

Section Seven — Answers 93

Published by Coordination Group Publications Ltd.
Illustrations by: Sandy Gardner, e-mail: illustrations@sandygardner.co.uk,
                       Bowser (Colorado USA), Ashley Tyson and Lex Ward.

Coordinated by Paddy Gannon

Contributors
Chris Christofi
Nigel Saunders

Design editor: Paul Thompson

Updated by:
Chris Dennett
Dominic Hall
James Paul Wallis
Suzanne Worthington

ISBN-10: 1 84146 616 6
ISBN-13: 978 1 84146 616 3

Groovy website: www.cgpbooks.co.uk

Jolly bits of clipart from CorelDRAW®
Printed by Elanders Hindson Ltd, Newcastle upon Tyne.

Questions on Cells

Q1 *Both the house and the human body are built up of smaller building blocks.*

    a) What do we call the building blocks that make up the:

      i) house? ....

      ii) human body? ....

Q2 a) Draw lines from the labels to the correct parts of both the plant and animal cell:

| cytoplasm | nucleus | cell membrane |

Animal Cell

Plant Cell

    b) Name two structures that are found in plant cells but not in animal cells.

....

Q3 Complete these sentences with the words in the list below:

| cell membrane | cell wall | chloroplasts | nucleus | sap vacuole |

All cells have a _____ around their cytoplasm and a

_____. Plant cells also have a strong _____

on their outside and _____ to make food. Plant cells also

have a _____ .

Q4 Write down whether these sentences are true or false:

    a) All cells have a membrane. ....

    b) All cells have a cell wall. ....

    c) Cell walls are made of starch. ....

    d) Cell walls are made of cellulose. ....

    e) Chromosomes are found in the cytoplasm. ....

Questions on Cells

Q5 *This is a diagram of a human sperm cell.*

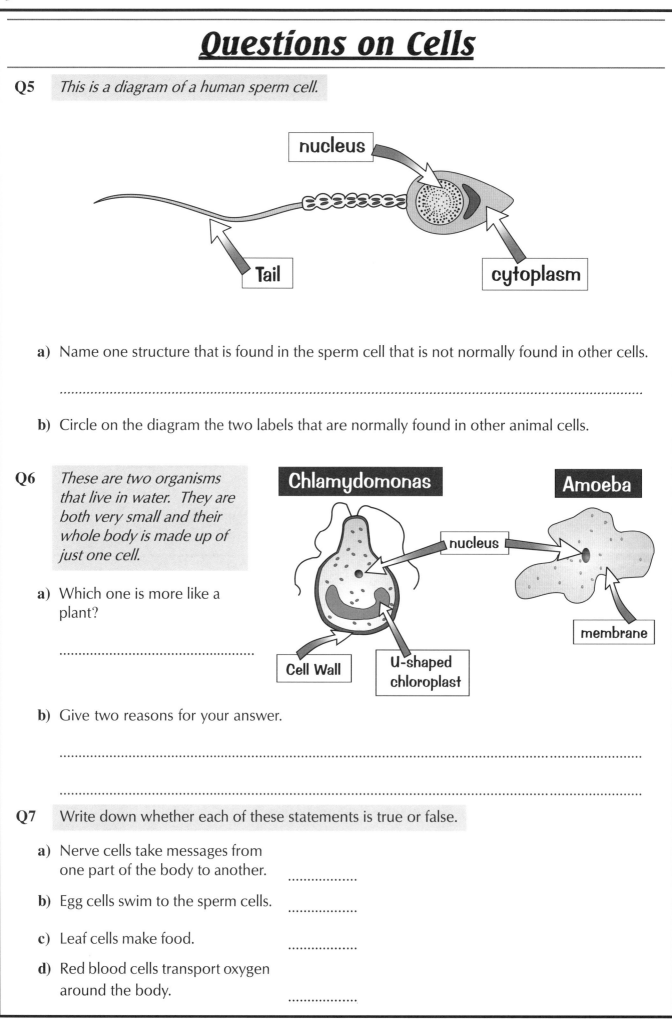

a) Name one structure that is found in the sperm cell that is not normally found in other cells.

....

b) Circle on the diagram the two labels that are normally found in other animal cells.

Q6 *These are two organisms that live in water. They are both very small and their whole body is made up of just one cell.*

a) Which one is more like a plant?

....

b) Give two reasons for your answer.

....

....

Q7 Write down whether each of these statements is true or false.

a) Nerve cells take messages from one part of the body to another. ....

b) Egg cells swim to the sperm cells. ....

c) Leaf cells make food. ....

d) Red blood cells transport oxygen around the body. ....

Questions on Specialised Cells

Q1   *Eggs are cells. The ostrich egg is the largest cell in the world.*

   a) Name three parts of an egg that make it a cell. ....

....

   b) What is the job of an egg cell?

....

Q2   These are cells that do special jobs.

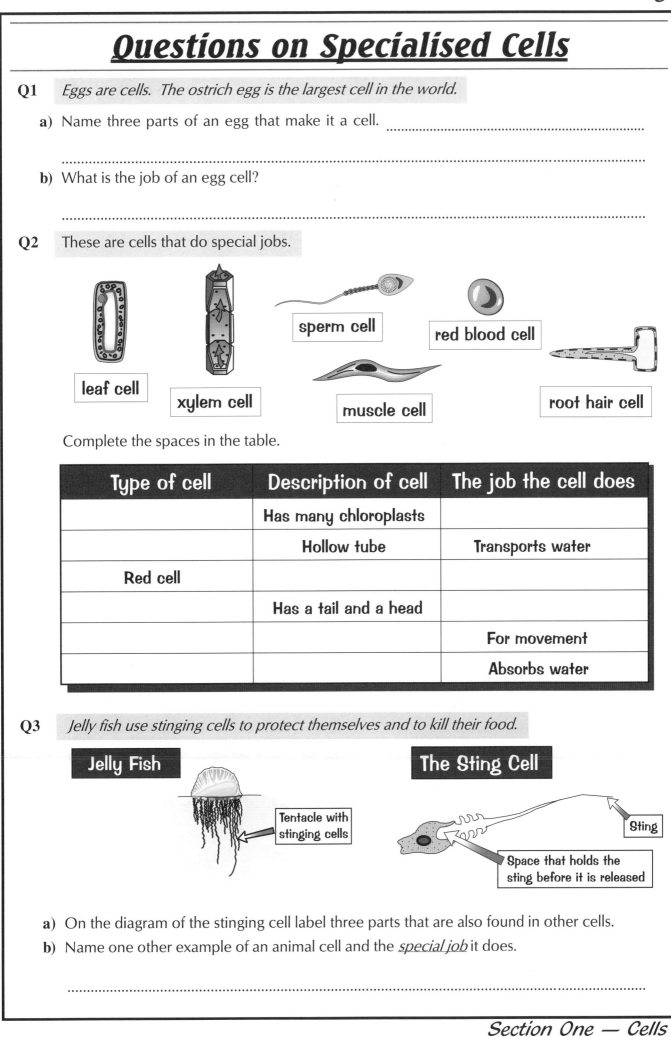

leaf cell

xylem cell

sperm cell

red blood cell

muscle cell

root hair cell

Complete the spaces in the table.

Type of cell	Description of cell	The job the cell does
	Has many chloroplasts	
	Hollow tube	Transports water
Red cell		
	Has a tail and a head	
		For movement
		Absorbs water

Q3   *Jelly fish use stinging cells to protect themselves and to kill their food.*

Jelly Fish

The Sting Cell

Tentacle with
stinging cells

Sting

Space that holds the
sting before it is released

   a) On the diagram of the stinging cell label three parts that are also found in other cells.

   b) Name one other example of an animal cell and the *special job* it does.

....

Questions on Diffusion

Q1   The diagram shows photosynthesis in a leaf. Gases go in and out of leaves by diffusion.

a) From the diagram, what colour are the arrows that represent the movement of a gas going into the leaf?

....

Which gas do these arrows represent?

....

b) What colour are the arrows that represent the movement of a gas going out of the leaf?

....

Which gas do these arrows represent?

....

Q2 a) *A droplet of coloured liquid was injected into some clear gelatin.*
The colour diffused through the gelatin.

Draw arrows on the diagram to show
where the colour spreads.

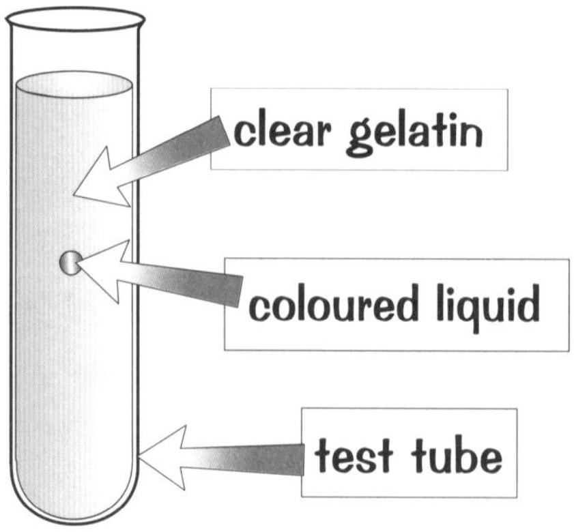

clear gelatin

coloured liquid

test tube

b) Give one example of diffusion in:

i) plants ....

....

ii) animals ....

....

Questions on Diffusion

Q3 *Gases diffuse (spread) from a high concentration (many particles) to a low concentration (few particles). This occurs in the air sacs in a lung (diagram opposite).*

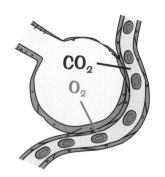

a) Draw arrow heads on the lines to show which way the oxygen and carbon dioxide particles move.

b) Complete the table by ticking the correct boxes.

Part of Lung	Concentration of oxygen		Concentration of carbon dioxide	
	Low (few particles)	High (many particles)	Low (few particles)	High (many particles)
Blood vessel going to lung				
Air sac				

Q4 *Diffusion is a very important process in living things. Many parts of living things have become adapted to make diffusion happen more quickly.*

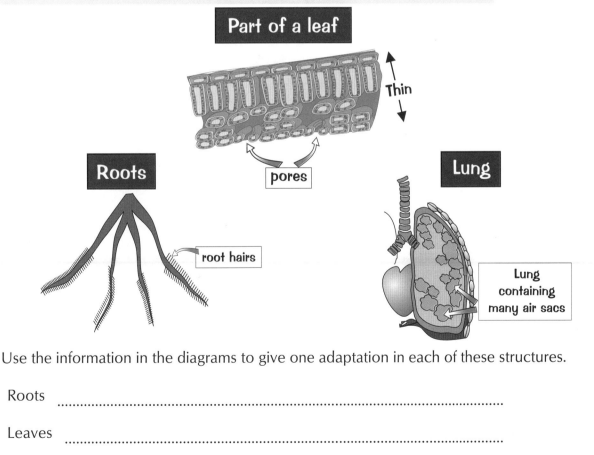

Use the information in the diagrams to give one adaptation in each of these structures.

a) Roots ....

b) Leaves ....

c) Lungs ....

Questions on Diffusion

Q5 *Some cotton wool was soaked in ammonia. The cotton wool was placed at one end of a glass tube. The ammonia turns the pieces of red litmus paper blue.*

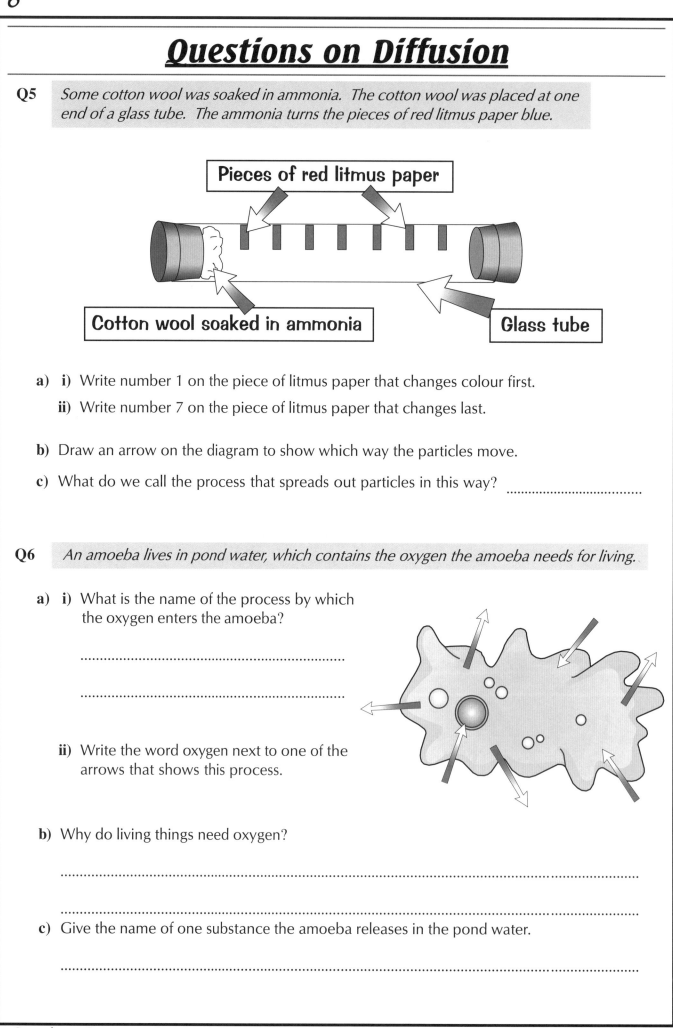

Pieces of red litmus paper

Cotton wool soaked in ammonia

Glass tube

a) i) Write number 1 on the piece of litmus paper that changes colour first.

   ii) Write number 7 on the piece of litmus paper that changes last.

b) Draw an arrow on the diagram to show which way the particles move.

c) What do we call the process that spreads out particles in this way? ....

Q6 *An amoeba lives in pond water, which contains the oxygen the amoeba needs for living.*

a) i) What is the name of the process by which the oxygen enters the amoeba?

   ....

   ....

   ii) Write the word oxygen next to one of the arrows that shows this process.

b) Why do living things need oxygen?

   ....

   ....

c) Give the name of one substance the amoeba releases in the pond water.

   ....

Questions on Plant Structure

Q1 *A plant is made up of three parts.*

a) Label parts A, B and C.

A ....

B ....

C ....

X —⟶

b) What do we call X? ....

c) Explain in one sentence what each part of the plant does.

A ....

B ....

C ....

Q2 Draw lines to connect the part of the plant with the correct function it does.

| Plant part | ⟹ | Function |

Plant part
stems
roots
leaves
flowers

Function
absorb water
carry leaves
make food
seeds are made here

Q3 Use the words to *fill in the spaces*.

flower   leaves   minerals   petals   roots   reproductive   seeds   stem   water

Plants are made up of three parts, the .... , the stem and the

.... which are found under the ground. The roots hold the plant

firmly in the ground. They also absorb .... with dissolved

.... from the soil. The .... has the job of holding the

plant upright. This helps the leaves to catch more light. The .... are

responsible for making food. The flowers contain the .... parts of the

plant. These are found inside the .... When the flower dies,

.... are released.

8

Questions on Plant Structure

Q4 *The diagram shows the parts of a cabbage plant that are eaten by pest animals.*

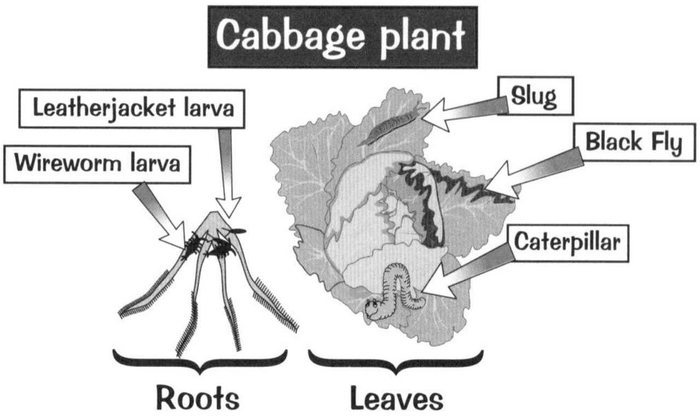

a) *More pest animals feed off the leaves than the roots.* Why do you think this is?

....

....

Cabbage plant

Leatherjacket larva

Wireworm larva

Slug

Black Fly

Caterpillar

Roots   Leaves

b) Why does the plant die when its roots are eaten?

....

....

c) Where would we find the animals that eat the roots of plants?

....

Q5 *The Colorado beetle has spread from Colorado in America to much of Europe. It has been found in the UK since 1901. Both the beetles and their larvae (caterpillar like animals) feed on the leaves of potato plants.*

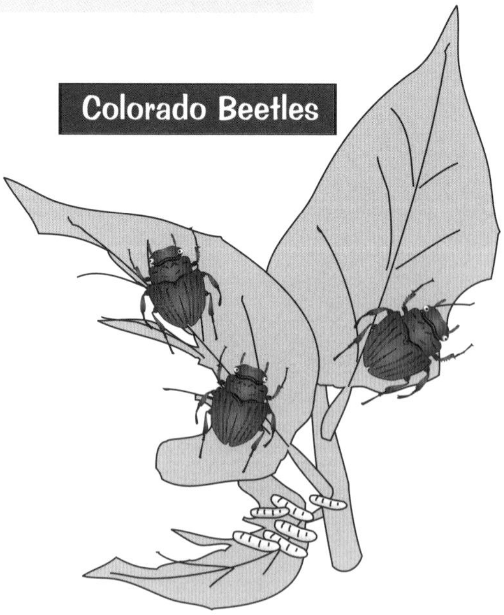

a) Why are leaves important to a plant?

....

....

....

Colorado Beetles

b) What happens to a plant if its leaves are eaten?

....

....

c) Name one other garden animal that eats leaves.

....

Section Two — Plants

Questions on Leaf Structure

Q1 *The diagram opposite shows part of a leaf.*

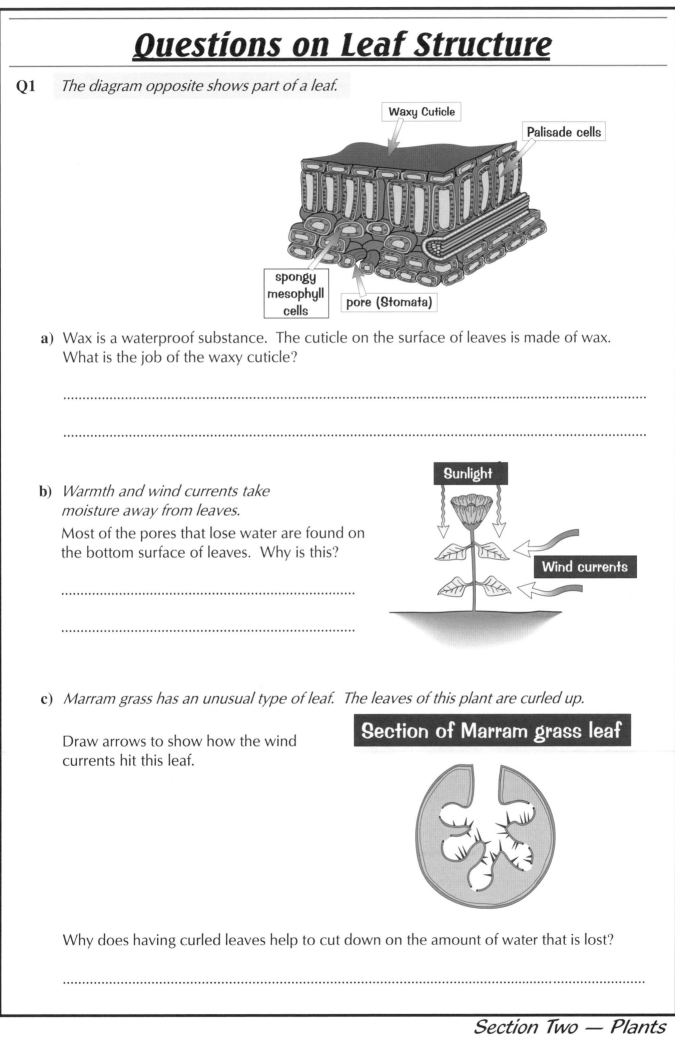

a) Wax is a waterproof substance. The cuticle on the surface of leaves is made of wax.
What is the job of the waxy cuticle?

....

....

b) *Warmth and wind currents take moisture away from leaves.*

Most of the pores that lose water are found on the bottom surface of leaves. Why is this?

....

....

c) *Marram grass has an unusual type of leaf. The leaves of this plant are curled up.*

Draw arrows to show how the wind currents hit this leaf.

Why does having curled leaves help to cut down on the amount of water that is lost?

....

Questions on Leaf Structure

Q2   *Plants whose leaves float on water have more pores on the top surface of their leaves.*

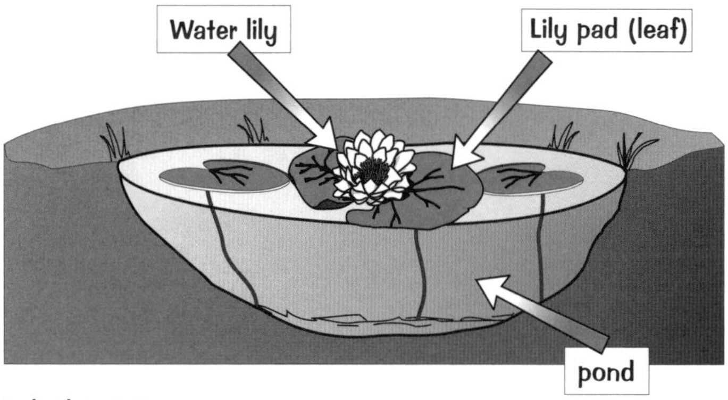

Water lily

Lily pad (leaf)

pond

Why do you think this is?

....

....

Q3   *Leaves are darker on their top surface. This is because they have more of the green substance, called chlorophyll, in the cells near the top surface.*

a) Light from the sun hits the leaves. Draw on the diagram opposite an arrow showing the direction the light is coming from.

b) Why is it better to have more of the green substance (Chlorophyll) in the top surface of the leaf?

....

....

Q4   Match the description on the left with the correct part of the leaf.

| description | ➞ | part |

green substance is called

they contain chlorophyll

cells that contain the green substance

chloroplasts

chlorophyll

leaf cells

Questions on Leaf Structure

Q5 *Some plants have green and white areas. This is called variegated leaves.*

Variegated geranium leaf

Green area

White area

Cross section of part of leaf

a) Draw an arrow on a leaf cell that is found in the white area and label it W.

b) Draw an arrow on a leaf cell that is found in the green area and label it G.

c) Why are some cells green?

....

....

Q6 Complete the following passage with the words below:

carbon dioxide chlorophyll chloroplasts light pores waxy cuticle xylem

Food is made in the leaves of the plant. Leaf cells have many ....

which contain the green substance .... This substance absorbs

.... The gas .... diffuses easily through spaces

inside the leaf cells. To make sugar, water is also needed. Water is taken to the leaf

by .... cells. To stop water being lost, the surface of the leaf is

covered by a .... To let gases move in and out of the

leaf, there are many .... These are called stomata and are

mainly found on the bottom surface of leaves.

Q7 Most of these words have something to do with leaves.
From each line of words, ring the one that does not.

a) leaf pores root waxy cuticle

b) carbon dioxide sulphuric acid oxygen water

c) chlorophyll sunlight food petals

d) veins bark pores chloroplasts

Section Two — Plants

Questions on Transpiration

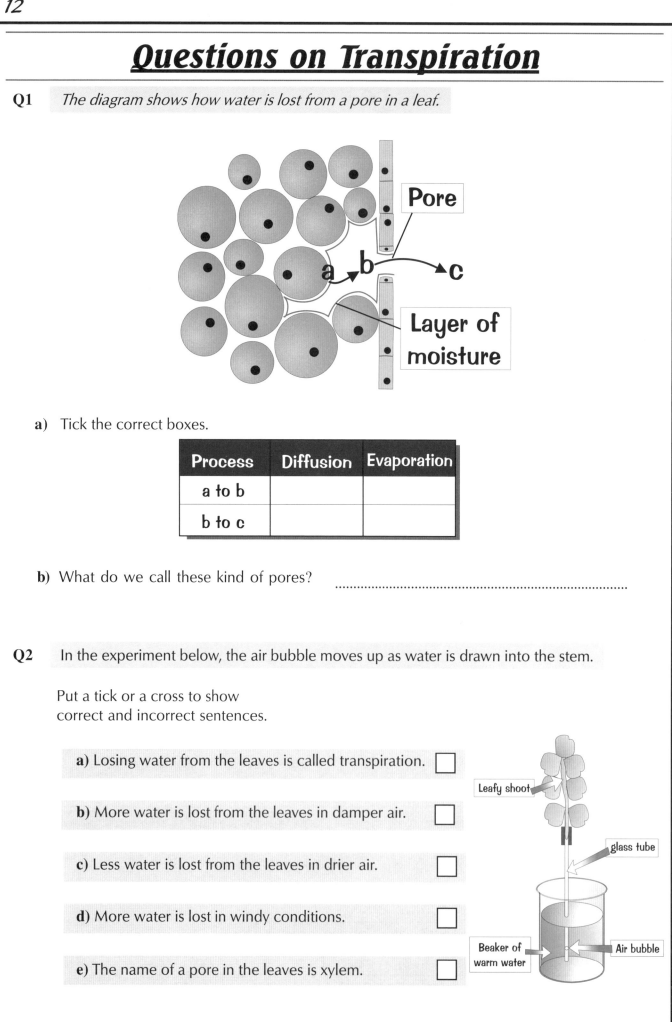

Q1 *The diagram shows how water is lost from a pore in a leaf.*

Pore

Layer of moisture

a) Tick the correct boxes.

Process	Diffusion	Evaporation
a to b		
b to c		

b) What do we call these kind of pores? ....

Q2 In the experiment below, the air bubble moves up as water is drawn into the stem.

Put a tick or a cross to show
correct and incorrect sentences.

a) Losing water from the leaves is called transpiration. ☐

b) More water is lost from the leaves in damper air. ☐

c) Less water is lost from the leaves in drier air. ☐

d) More water is lost in windy conditions. ☐

e) The name of a pore in the leaves is xylem. ☐

Leafy shoot

glass tube

Beaker of warm water

Air bubble

Questions on Transpiration

Q3 *This experiment shows water being lost from a clay pot.*
Clay pots have a large number of tiny holes.

a) How is the pot similar to a leaf?

....

b) Give one way that the pot is different from the leaf.

....

c) Say how each of these conditions affects the amount
of water lost from the pot.

i) very damp air ....

ii) very hot air ....

iii) air that is not moving ....

Clay Pot with tiny holes

Water

Capillary tube

Air bubble

Beaker of warm water

Q4 *Before a cutting grows roots, you often remove its leaves and cover it with a plastic bag.*
Without roots, plants find it difficult to get enough water.

a) Where do plants get their water from?

....

b) Why does it help the plant if we remove the leaves?

....

c) Why do we place a plastic bag around a cutting?

....

....

....

Plastic bag

Stem cutting with no leaves

Q5 Find the following words in the word search.

XYLEM
STOMATA
LEAVES
WILTING
TRANSPIRATION

E	A	B	Z	K	X	X	O	P	Q	A	J	H	I
P	O	B	T	S	Y	Y	K	S	E	A	U	U	F
Q	Z	B	O	K	L	Z	T	E	J	G	G	W	V
I	H	M	N	L	E	O	R	J	B	N	T	E	W
J	I	N	M	O	M	D	Q	C	S	I	S	M	R
O	L	L	E	A	V	E	S	I	E	T	D	Z	X
O	H	T	T	M	U	U	Z	H	R	L	Q	N	Y
T	R	A	N	S	P	I	R	A	T	I	O	N	P
T	P	P	O	O	A	Y	S	K	P	W	L	M	O

Questions on Transport Systems in Plants

Q1 *Plants get their water from the soil. This water is later lost to the atmosphere.*

a) Use these words to complete the flow diagram.

leaves	roots	stem

SOIL ➡ _____ ➡ _____ ➡ _____ ➡ ATMOSPHERE

b) i) What cells transport water? ....

   ii) What else do these cells carry? ....

c) What cells carry sugar (dissolved food)? ....

Q2 *The diagram shows the path water takes through a plant.*

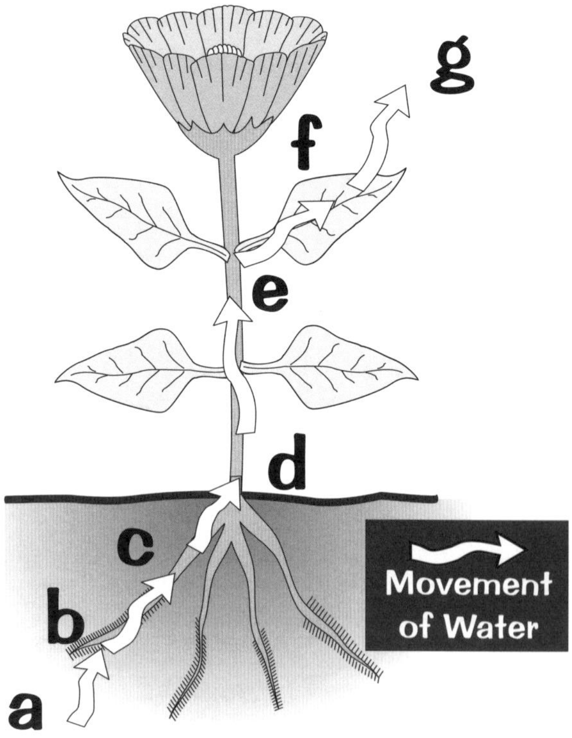

a) What carries water from **d** to **f**?

....

b) To get to **g**, water escapes from little holes in the leaves.

   i) What are these holes called?

   ....

   ii) What do we call this process?

   ....

c) Food is made in the leaves and stored in the roots.

   i) What cells carry the food?

   ....

   ii) Draw arrows to show the journey of the food.

   iii) Colour the arrows showing the journey of food in red and the journey of water in blue.

   iv) Add a key of all the arrows to the diagram.

Movement of Water

Questions on Transport Systems in Plants

Q3 *This is a diagram of a plum tree. The plums are full of sugar which is made in the leaves of the tree.*

a) How does the sugar get from the leaves to the plums?

....

....

....

The reason fruits like plums are swollen is because they are also full of water.

b) **i)** Where did the water originally come from?

....

ii) How does the water get to the plum fruits?

....

Q4 *Opposite is a section of a stem, showing the xylem and phloem cells.*

phloem cell

xylem cell

a) What is the job of the xylem cells?

....

....

b) What is the job of the phloem cells?

....

c) Why do the ends of the xylem and phloem cells have a large opening?

....

d) Why are xylem and phloem cells hollow?

....

e) Why are xylem and phloem cells sometimes called the 'plumbing' of the plant?

....

Questions on Photosynthesis

Q1 *The diagram shows what the leaves need to make food.*

a) Use the words in the box below to fill in the
blanks on the diagram.

chlorophyll	air
oxygen	air
carbon dioxide	
sunlight	water

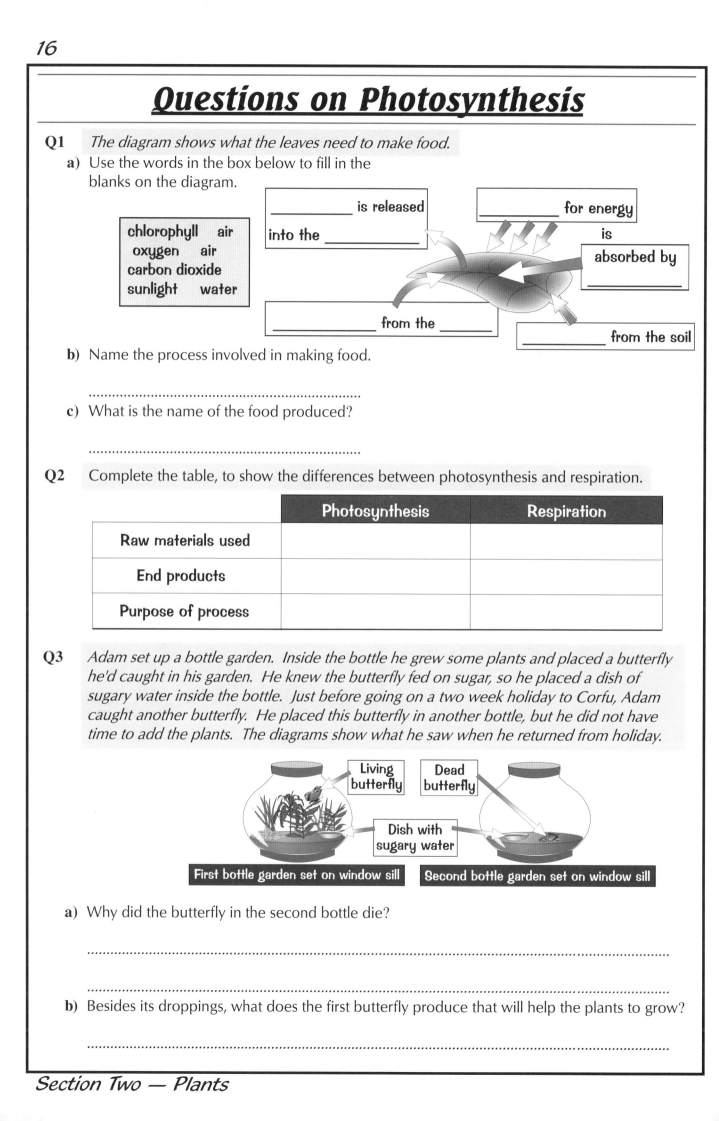

_____ is released
into the _____

_____ for energy
is
absorbed by
_____

_____ from the _____

_____ from the soil

b) Name the process involved in making food.

....

c) What is the name of the food produced?

....

Q2 Complete the table, to show the differences between photosynthesis and respiration.

	Photosynthesis	Respiration
Raw materials used		
End products		
Purpose of process		

Q3 *Adam set up a bottle garden. Inside the bottle he grew some plants and placed a butterfly he'd caught in his garden. He knew the butterfly fed on sugar, so he placed a dish of sugary water inside the bottle. Just before going on a two week holiday to Corfu, Adam caught another butterfly. He placed this butterfly in another bottle, but he did not have time to add the plants. The diagrams show what he saw when he returned from holiday.*

Living
butterfly

Dead
butterfly

Dish with
sugary water

First bottle garden set on window sill

Second bottle garden set on window sill

a) Why did the butterfly in the second bottle die?

....

....

b) Besides its droppings, what does the first butterfly produce that will help the plants to grow?

....

Questions on Nutrition

Q1   Complete the sentences below about three nutrients. Choose the correct words from this list.

cell membranes	growth	energy	proteins	fats

Carbohydrates are needed to provide .... for the body.

.... are needed for .... and repair.

Energy is supplied by .... , which are also needed to make

....

Q2   *You should be able to remember foods that are good sources of the three main nutrients.*

a) Write down two examples of foods that are good sources of *carbohydrate*.

Food 1 ....   Food 2 ....

b) Write down two examples of foods that are good sources of *protein*.

Food 1 ....   Food 2 ....

c) Write down two examples of foods that are good sources of *fat*.

Food 1 ....   Food 2 ....

Q3   *We need 20–30g of dietary fibre (roughage) a day.*
A can of baked beans contains over 20g of dietary fibre.

a) Put a tick ✓ in the box ☐ next to each correct sentence about dietary fibre:

☐ Dietary fibre is needed to provide our bodies with carbohydrates for energy.

☐ Dietary fibre helps to prevent constipation if we eat enough of it.

☐ Raw fruit and vegetables are good sources of dietary fibre.

b) One sentence is incorrect. Write down a correct version of it in the space below.

....

Q4   *It is often recommended that we drink plenty of water, and some foods also contain water.*

Why is water so important in our diet?

....

Questions on Food Tests

Q1   Match the four substances to the correct test which identifies the substance.

| substance | ⟹ | indicator test |

fat can be detected using		Benedict's reagent
protein can be detected using		the emulsion test
starch can be detected using		the Biuret test
sugars can be detected using		iodine solution

Q2   Iodine solution is used in food tests. What colour would you see when it is added to:

a) Sugar?   ....

b) Starch?   ....

c) Protein?   ....

Q3   In the table below, complete the starting colour and
end result for a _positive test_ using Benedict's reagent.

colour at start

⬇

end result

....

....

Q4   Complete the instructions for the biuret test below. Choose from this list of words:

| purple   shake   sodium hydroxide   protein   copper sulphate |

The biuret test can be used to detect protein in food. You put some food in a test tube,

and add some .... You then give it a .... ,

and add some .... (this is blue). If it goes a

.... colour, it means that .... is present.

Section Three — Human Biology Part One

Questions on The Digestive System

Q1 Use the information below to name these parts of the digestive system. One has been done for you.

Name	Appearance
large intestine	Broad rippled tube
gullet	Long tube leading from the mouth to the stomach
pancreas	Gland with rippled edges
small intestine	Coiled narrow tube, 3-5cm in diameter, about 6-7m long
stomach	Large container for food - holds about 1 litre

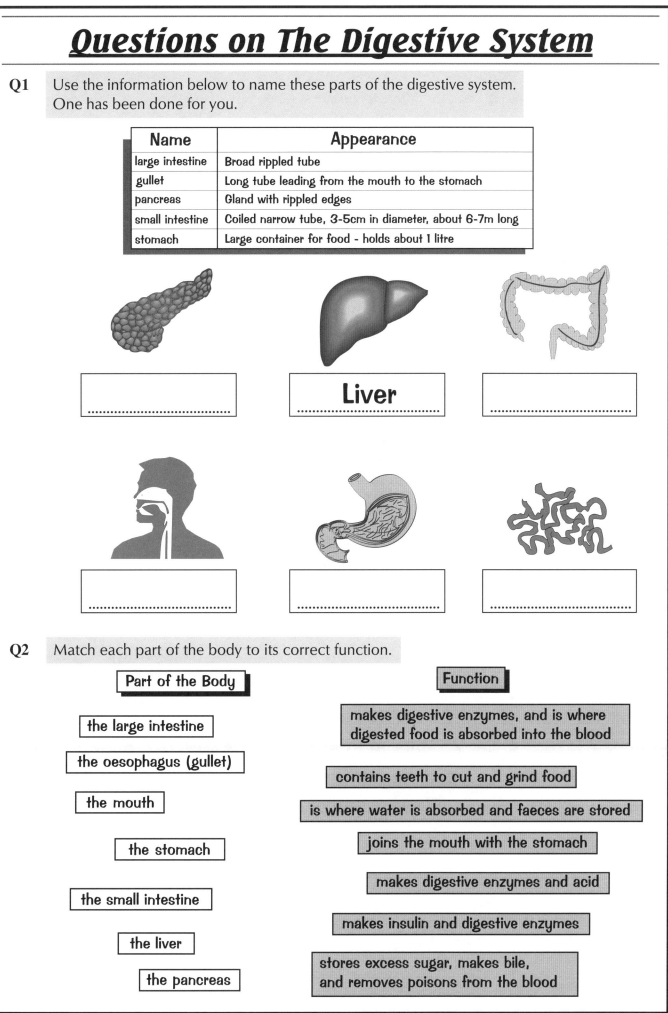

....

Liver

....

....

....

....

....

Q2 Match each part of the body to its correct function.

Part of the Body

the large intestine

the oesophagus (gullet)

the mouth

the stomach

the small intestine

the liver

the pancreas

Function

makes digestive enzymes, and is where digested food is absorbed into the blood

contains teeth to cut and grind food

is where water is absorbed and faeces are stored

joins the mouth with the stomach

makes digestive enzymes and acid

makes insulin and digestive enzymes

stores excess sugar, makes bile, and removes poisons from the blood

Questions on The Digestive System

Q3 Write the names of each part of the digestive system in the correct boxes below. Choose from the words in the box at the bottom of the page. One of them, the gall bladder, has been done for you.

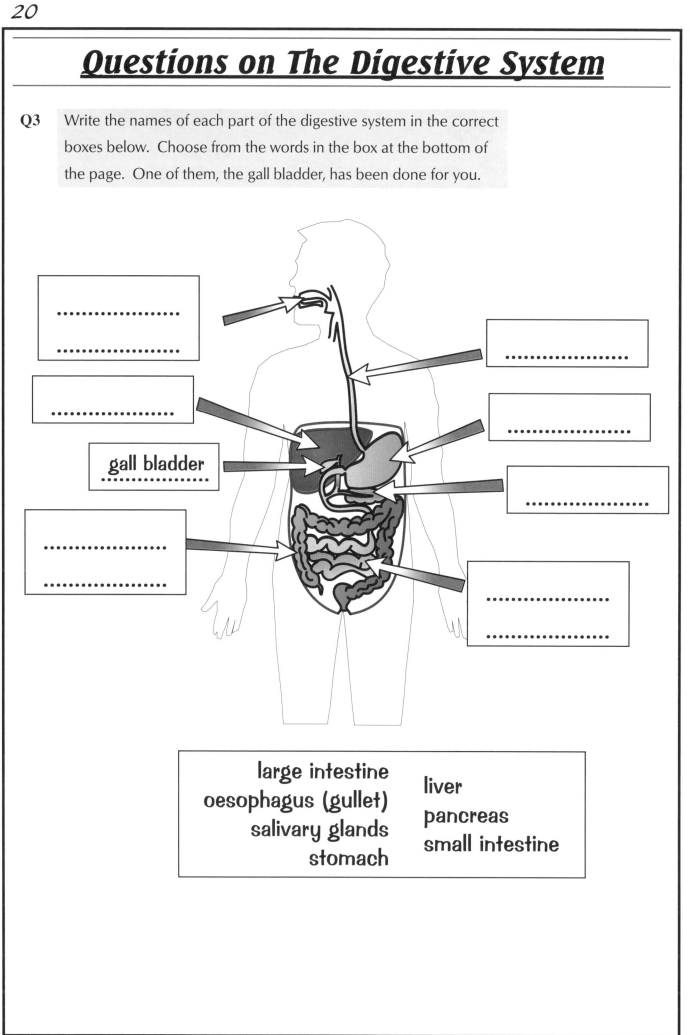

gall bladder

large intestine	
oesophagus (gullet)	liver
salivary glands	pancreas
stomach	small intestine

Questions on The Digestive System

Q4 Complete this crossword using the clues given below.

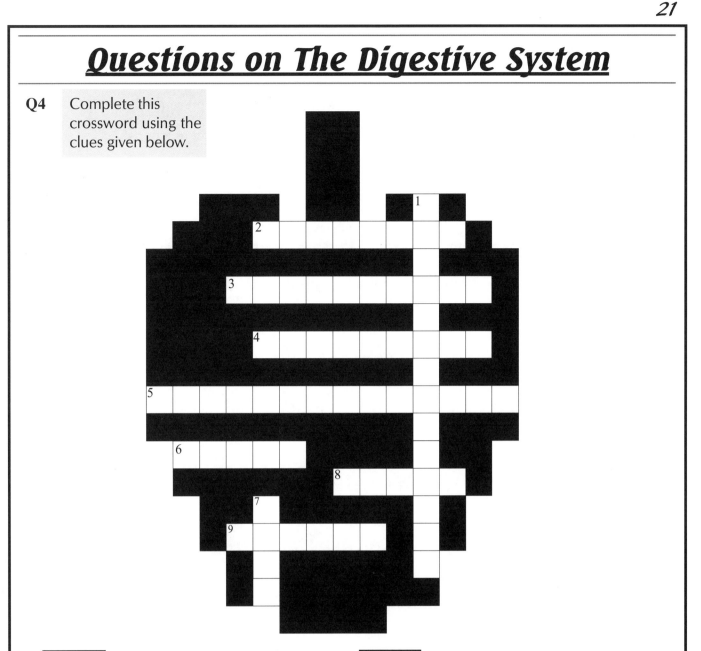

Across

2. Insulin and digestive enzymes are made here (8)

3. The gullet by another name (10)

4. The process by which food is broken down into small particles for absorption into the bloodstream (9)

5. Absorption of broken down food happens here (5,9)

6. This organ makes bile (5)

8. Look after them — they start the process of digestion (5)

9. Produces hydrochloric acid (7)

Down

1. Faeces are stored here before going out of the anus (5,9)

7. This is broken down by the digestive system (4)

Questions on Digestive Enzymes

Q1   Circle the correct words from each underlined pair in the following sentences:

   a) A catalyst is a substance that is produced by / speeds up chemical reactions.

   b) A catalyst is used up / not used up during the reaction. It can be used only once /

   more than once.

   c) Different reactions need the same catalyst / different catalysts. Enzymes are

   artificial / biological catalysts. Enzymes are proteins / metals.

Q2 a) Put a tick in the box next to each correct sentence about digestion:

   ☐ In digestion, large molecules are broken down into small molecules.

   ☐ Digestive enzymes slow down digestion.

   ☐ The digestive system provides the right conditions for digestive enzymes to work well.

   b) One sentence is incorrect. Write down a correct version of it in the space below.

   ....

   ....

Q3   *Gastric juice is added to food when it reaches the stomach. This juice contains an acid.*

   a) Name the acid secreted by the stomach.

   ....

   b) Estimate the pH of the stomach contents and give a reason for your answer.

   ....

   c) Give two reasons why the stomach secretes this acid

   ....

   ....

Questions on Digestive Enzymes

Q4 *You need to know about <u>three</u> types of digestive enzymes.*

Match the digestive enzymes to the substance that they break down:

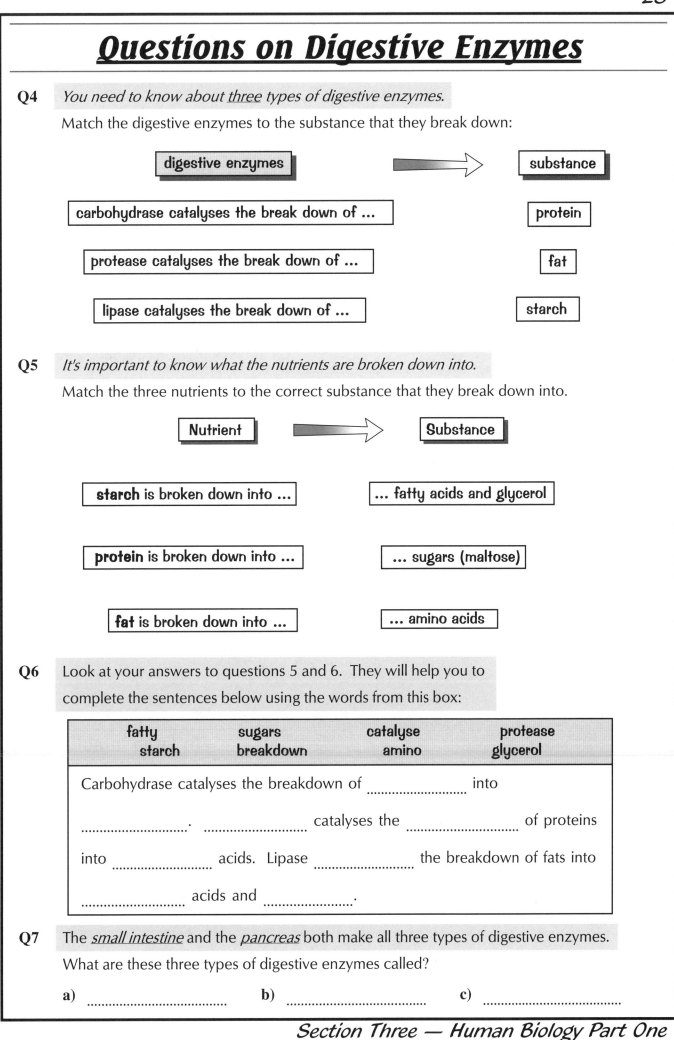

digestive enzymes

substance

carbohydrase catalyses the break down of ...

protein

protease catalyses the break down of ...

fat

lipase catalyses the break down of ...

starch

Q5 *It's important to know what the nutrients are broken down into.*

Match the three nutrients to the correct substance that they break down into.

Nutrient

Substance

starch is broken down into ...

... fatty acids and glycerol

protein is broken down into ...

... sugars (maltose)

fat is broken down into ...

... amino acids

Q6 Look at your answers to questions 5 and 6. They will help you to complete the sentences below using the words from this box:

fatty	sugars	catalyse	protease
starch	breakdown	amino	glycerol

Carbohydrase catalyses the breakdown of .... into

.... catalyses the .... of proteins

into .... acids. Lipase .... the breakdown of fats into

.... acids and ....

Q7 The <u>*small intestine*</u> and the <u>*pancreas*</u> both make all three types of digestive enzymes.

What are these three types of digestive enzymes called?

a) ....   b) ....   c) ....

Section Three — Human Biology Part One

Questions on Digestive Enzymes

Q9   The diagram below is a flow chart for the digestive system.

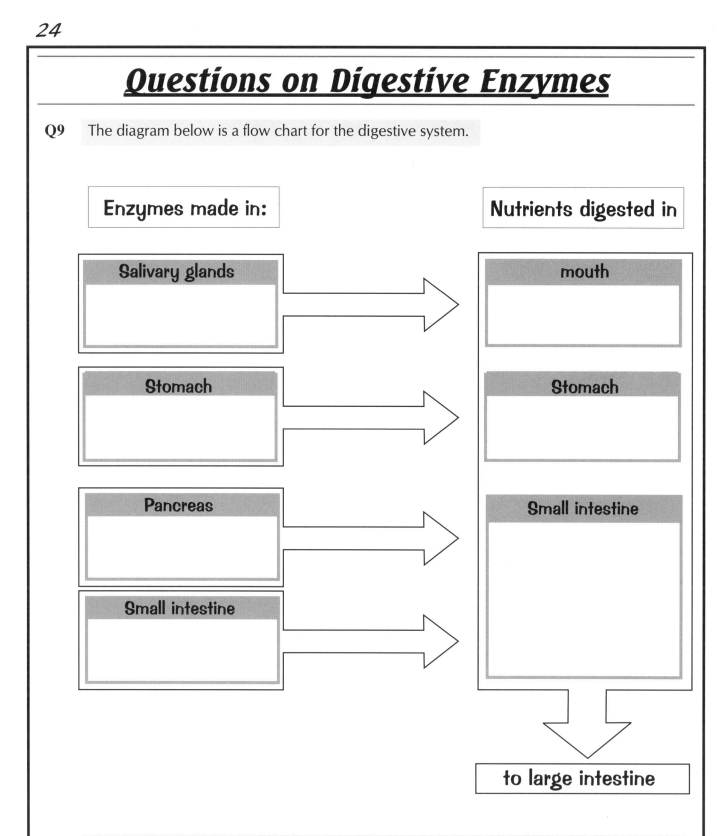

Enzymes made in:

Salivary glands

Stomach

Pancreas

Small intestine

Nutrients digested in

mouth

Stomach

Small intestine

to large intestine

a) In the boxes in the "enzymes" column, write down the name of each enzyme produced by the salivary glands, the stomach, the pancreas, and the small intestine.

b) In the boxes in the "nutrients" column, write down the name of each nutrient digested.

Questions on Absorption of Food

Q1   Angela was given a mixture of sand and sugar in a beaker.
She was asked to separate the sand from the sugar. Angela decided
to use the methods shown in the diagrams below to do this.

a) In steps 1 and 2, what happens to the sand?

....

....

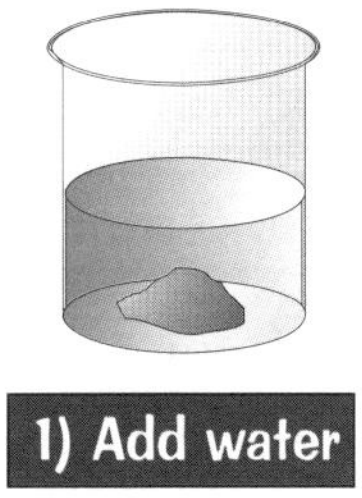

1) Add water

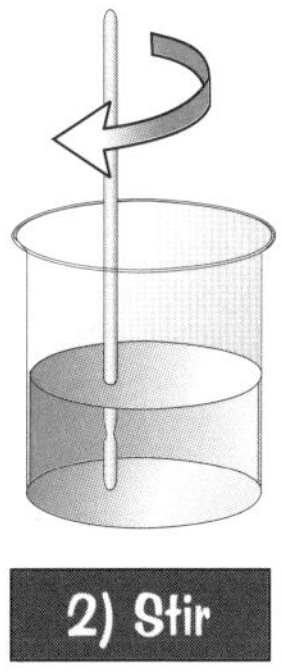

b) At the end of step 3, where will Angela find
the sand?

....

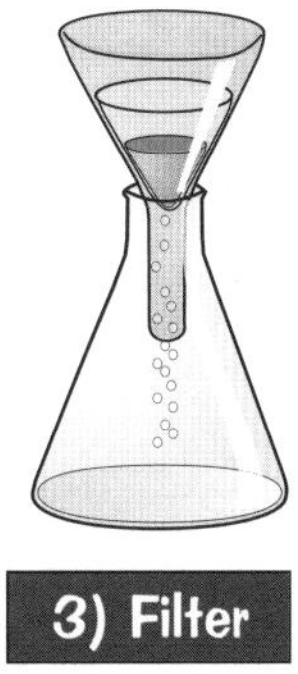

2) Stir

c) In steps 1 and 2, what happens to the sugar?

....

d) At the end of step 3, where will Angela find the sugar?

....

3) Filter

e) The pores in filter paper are so tiny that for particles to pass throught it they must be
dissolved in water. Why can sand be separated from sugar using Angela's method?

....

....

Q2   Put these substances into the correct columns in the table.
Some substances are already in the table for you.

| amino acids | starch | fat | sugar | fatty acids |

soluble (dissolve in water)	insoluble (do not dissolve in water)
some proteins	some proteins
glycerol	

Section Three — Human Biology Part One

Questions on Absorption of Food

Q3 *The digestive system breaks down food into small molecules that dissolve in water.*

For revision, match the food being digested to the correct substance that is created.

| Food being digested | ⟶ | Substance |

starch is digested to form...   amino acids

protein is digested to form...   sugar

fat is digested to form...   fatty acids and glycerol

Q4 Solve the absorption crossword.

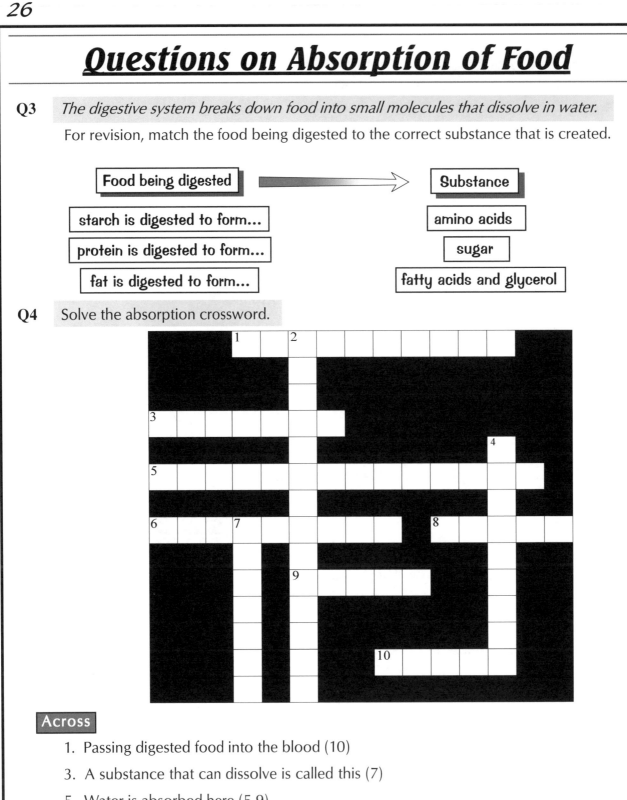

Across

1. Passing digested food into the blood (10)

3. A substance that can dissolve is called this (7)

5. Water is absorbed here (5,9)

6. The break down of food into small particles (9)

8. Digested food is absorbed into this (5)

9. This size of particle can be absorbed (5)

10. This size of particle can't be absorbed (5)

Down

2. Digested food is absorbed here (5,9)

4. Substances that can't dissolve are this (9)

7. These help make small molecules from large ones (7)

Section Three — Human Biology Part One

Questions on The Circulatory System

Q1 *There are two main components of the circulatory system. One organ has a circuit all to itself and its* <u>artery</u> *carries* <u>deoxygenated</u> *blood. Which organ is this?*

....

Q2 a) Put a tick in the box next to each correct sentence about the circulatory system:

☐ The circulatory system transports oxygen from the cells to the lungs.

☐ The circulatory system distributes heat and hormones around the body.

☐ The circulatory system transports wastes away from the cells in the body.

b) Write down a correct version of the incorrect sentence in the space below.

....

Q3 *The diagram below shows the main features of the circulatory system. Deoxygenated blood is represented by grey lines, and deoxygenated blood by black lines. The arrows show the direction of movement of the blood.*

Use your knowledge and the clues in the diagram to match the labels 1 – 3 with the following blood vessels:

Blood vessels:	Pulmonary vein	Aorta	Vena cava

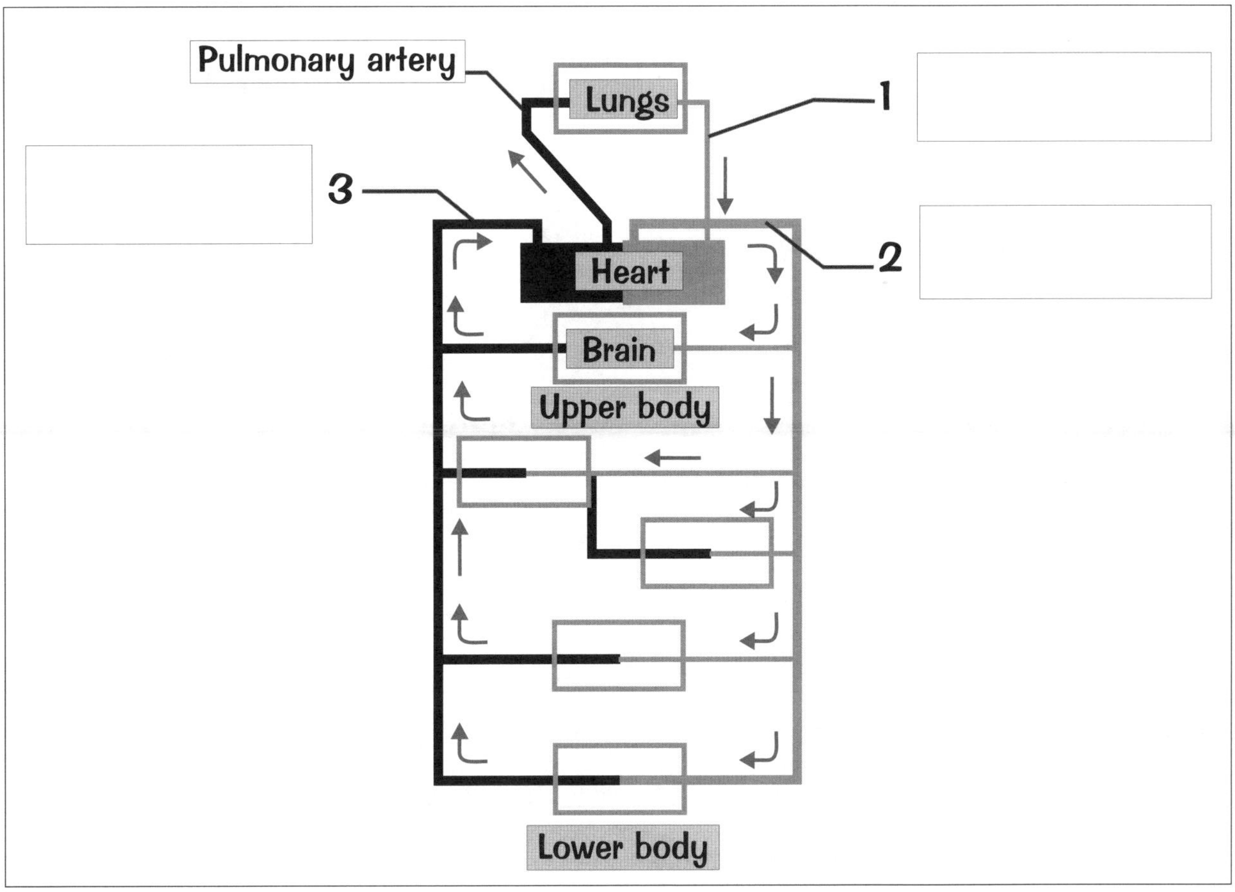

Pulmonary artery

Lungs

1

3

Heart

2

Brain

Upper body

Lower body

Questions on The Circulatory System

Q4 From the evidence in the diagram and your answers in Question 3, what is the difference between an *artery* and a *vein?* Put a tick in the box next to the correct sentence:

☐ Arteries carry oxygenated blood and veins carry deoxygenated blood.

☐ Veins carry oxygenated blood and arteries carry deoxygenated blood.

☐ Arteries carry blood from the heart and veins carry blood to the heart.

☐ Veins carry blood from the heart and arteries carry blood to the heart.

Q5 What is the function of the heart in the circulatory system?

....

Q6 Why is this system called the circulatory system?

....

Q7 *The diagram on the right shows the human heart drawn as a simple engineering drawing, rather than as a cross-section of a real heart.*

— The arrows show the movement of blood.
— The valves are shown in grey.

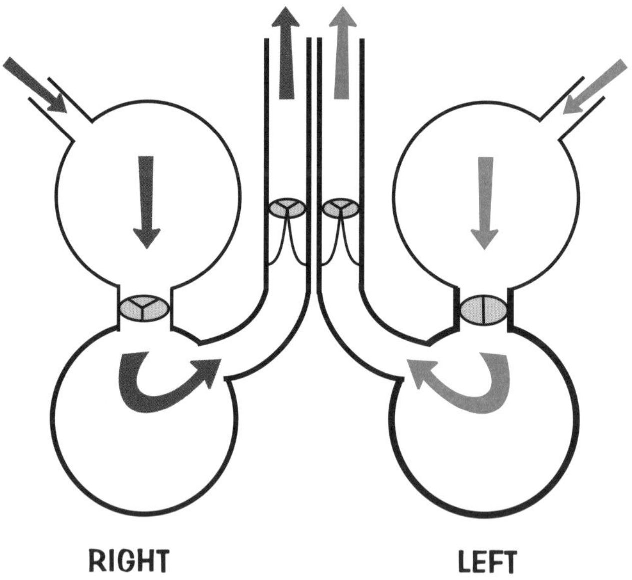

RIGHT   **LEFT**

Circle the correct answers in the questions below.

a) There are 1 / 2 / 3 / 4 chambers in the heart.

b) The upper chambers are called <u>ventricles</u> / <u>atria</u>.

c) The lower chambers are called <u>ventricles</u> / <u>atria</u>.

d) Deoxygenated blood returns from the body to the <u>left</u> / <u>right</u> side of the heart.

e) Oxygenated blood returns from the lungs to the <u>left</u> / <u>right</u> side of the heart.

f) The <u>valves</u> / <u>muscles</u> in the heart make sure that blood flows in the right direction.

Questions on The Heart

Q1 *You may be asked to label the parts of the heart. The diagram below shows a cross-section of the human heart drawn from the front.* Match the labels to the correct names:

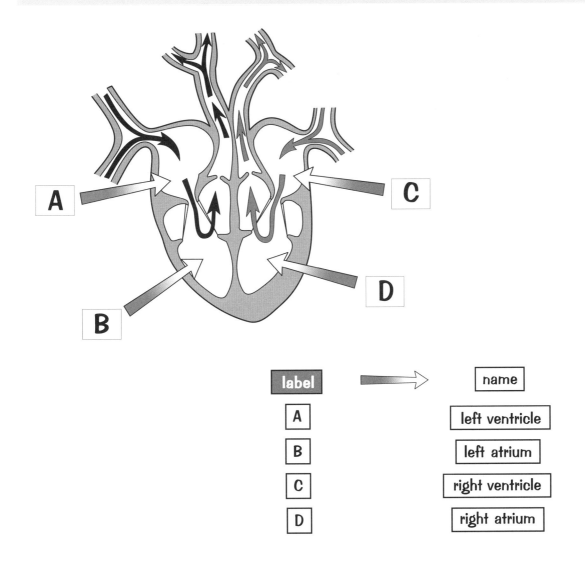

label		name
A		left ventricle
B		left atrium
C		right ventricle
D		right atrium

Q2 *The diagram below shows a cross-section of the human heart, drawn from the front.*
Write down these four blood vessels in the correct boxes to complete the labelling.

pulmonary vein

aorta

vena cava

pulmonary artery

Questions on The Heart

Q3 Complete these sentences about the heart.
Choose from the list of words below.

valves	muscle	body	blood	pumps	wall

The .... of the heart is mainly .... The heart .... blood around the .... The .... prevent backflow of ....

Q4 *The diagram on the right shows the way the heart fits into the circulatory system.*
The left side pumps blood around the body.

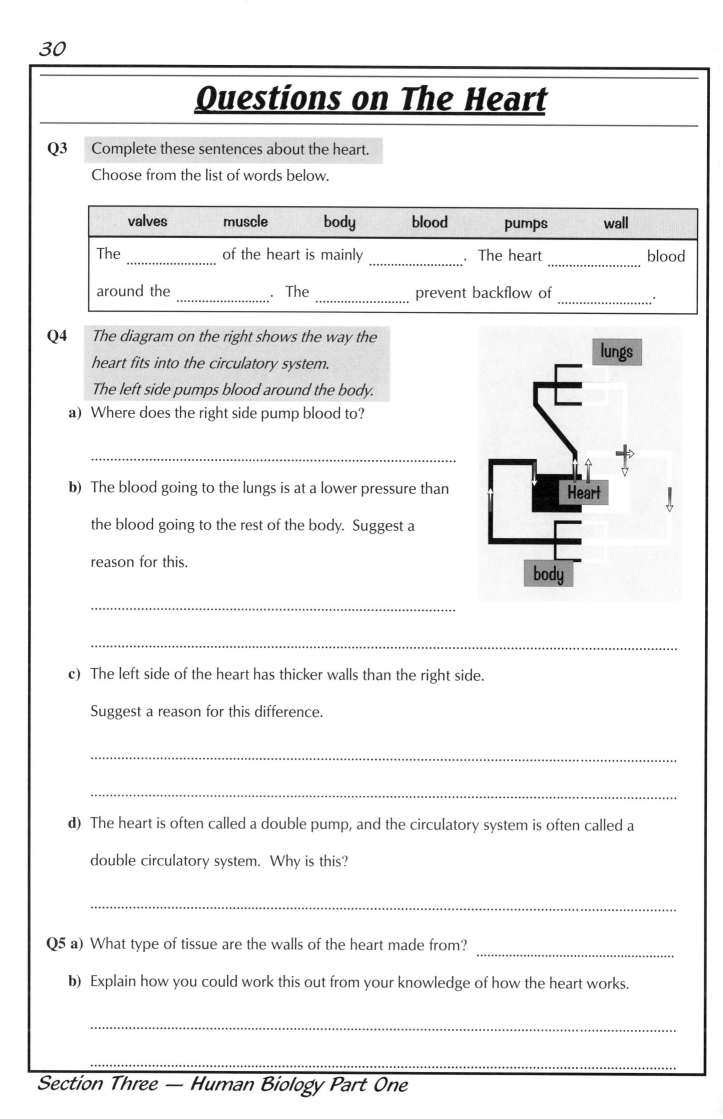

a) Where does the right side pump blood to?

....

b) The blood going to the lungs is at a lower pressure than the blood going to the rest of the body. Suggest a reason for this.

....

....

c) The left side of the heart has thicker walls than the right side.

Suggest a reason for this difference.

....

....

d) The heart is often called a double pump, and the circulatory system is often called a double circulatory system. Why is this?

....

Q5 a) What type of tissue are the walls of the heart made from? ....

b) Explain how you could work this out from your knowledge of how the heart works.

....

....

Questions on The Heart

Q6 The sentences below describe the steps needed for the heart to pump blood.
Put a ring around the correct options of <u>underlined</u> words.

Blood enters the heart via [<u>the left</u> / <u>the right</u> / <u>either</u>] [<u>atrium</u> / <u>ventricle</u>].

Blood leaves the heart when either [<u>atrium</u> / <u>ventricle</u>] [<u>contracts</u> / <u>relaxes</u>].

Valves make sure that the [<u>blood</u> / <u>air</u>] flows in the correct direction.

Contractions of the right atrium force blood into the [<u>left</u> / <u>right</u>] [<u>artery</u> / <u>ventricle</u>].

The pulmonary vein is odd in that it carries [<u>oxygenated</u> / <u>deoxygenated</u>] blood

Q7 Complete the crossword. The word answers are all to do with the heart.

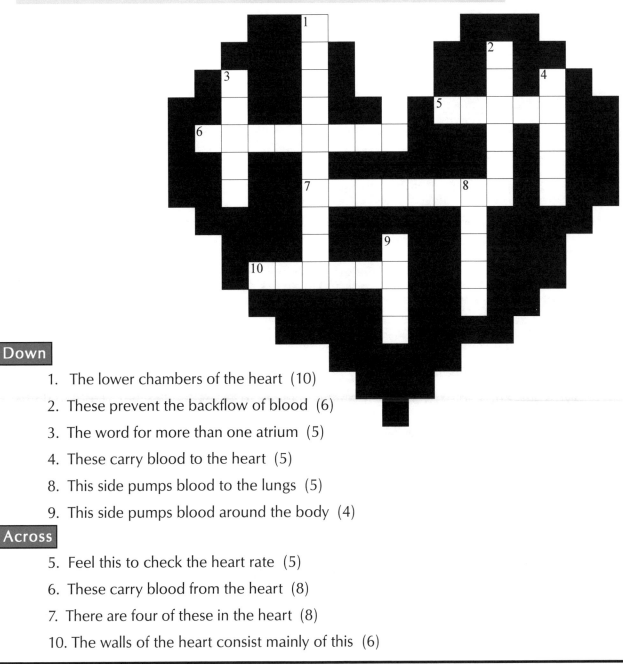

Down

1. The lower chambers of the heart (10)
2. These prevent the backflow of blood (6)
3. The word for more than one atrium (5)
4. These carry blood to the heart (5)
8. This side pumps blood to the lungs (5)
9. This side pumps blood around the body (4)

Across

5. Feel this to check the heart rate (5)
6. These carry blood from the heart (8)
7. There are four of these in the heart (8)
10. The walls of the heart consist mainly of this (6)

Section Three — Human Biology Part One

Questions on Blood Vessels

Q1 Circle the correct words in the <u>underlined</u> pairs in these two sentences about blood vessels.

Arteries carry blood <u>to</u> / <u>from</u> the heart at <u>low</u> / <u>high</u> pressure.

Veins carry blood <u>to</u> / <u>from</u> the heart at <u>low</u> / <u>high</u> pressure.

Q2 *The diagrams on the right show cross-sections of blood vessels. They are not drawn to scale.*

Endothelium

Elastic fibres and smooth muscle

Fibrous coat

A   B

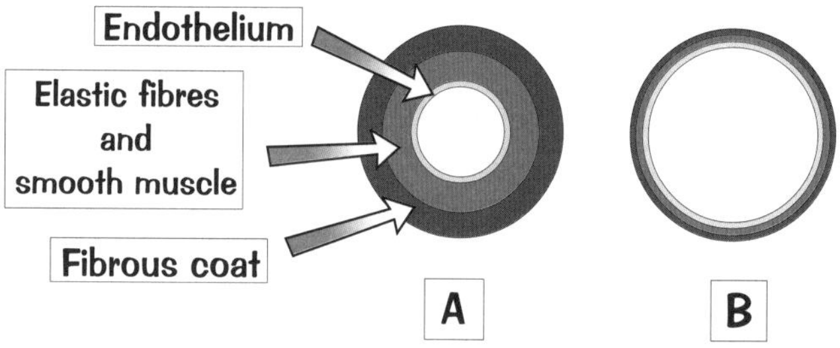

a) What is the space at the centre called?

....

b) One of these blood vessels is an artery, and one is a vein. Which diagram shows an artery?

Diagram   ....

c) Briefly explain how you worked out your answer to part b).

....

....

Q3 *The diagrams A and B opposite show pieces of artery and vein sliced along their length. They are not drawn to scale.*

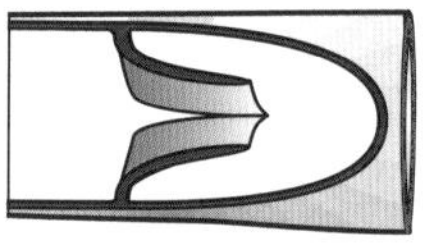

a) Which diagram, A or B, shows the vein? Diagram   ....

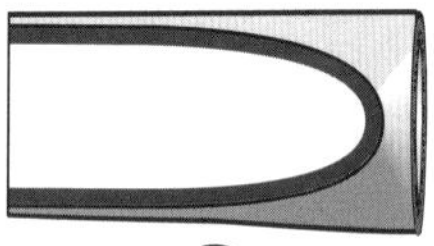

b) What is the name of the extra structure in diagram **A**?

....

A

c) What does the structure named in part b) do?

....

B

d) It is possible to work out which way the blood must be flowing in vessel A.
   Work this out, and draw an arrow on the diagram to show the direction of blood flow.

Q4 Complete the sentences below about *capillaries* using the words from this list:

capillaries	out	thin	vessels	narrow	blood	cells

Capillaries are very .... blood .... with ....

walls. Substances needed by the cells pass .... of the ....

through the capillary walls. Substances made by the .... can also pass into

the blood through the walls of the ....

Q5 Which type of blood vessel is the one that gives us a pulse? ....

Section Three — Human Biology Part One

Questions on The Blood

Q1   Match the type of blood cell to the correct description of its function

| Blood cell | ⟹ | Function |

red blood cells

platelets

white blood cells

help blood to clot at the site of a wound

transport oxygen from the lungs to the organs

ingest bacteria in the blood

Q2 a) Put a tick in the box next to each correct sentence about _plasma_:

☐ Plasma is a red coloured liquid.

☐ Plasma transports breakdown products of digestion.

☐ Plasma transports oxygen from the lungs to the organs.

☐ Plasma transports platelets.

☐ Plasma transports urea from the liver to the kidneys.

b)   Two sentences are incorrect. Write down correct versions of them in the spaces below.

....

....

c)   Plasma has other functions that are not listed in part a). Give another function of plasma.

....

Q3   _Three components of the blood consist of cells or fragments of cells._

a) Write down their names.

1 ....   2 ....   3 ....

b) Only one of these components has a nucleus. Which one? ....

c) The diagram on the right shows one of the cells named in part b).
Write down the names of the parts labelled A, B and C.

Part A   ....

Part B   ....

Part C   ....

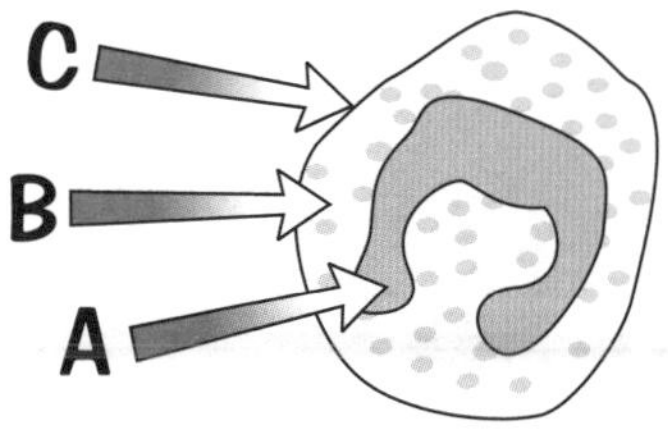

Q4   _Red cells have a shape called a_ biconcave _disc (look at the diagram of a cut away red cell)._
This gives them a large surface area for their volume.

a) Explain how this shape helps the red cell to do its job well.

....

....

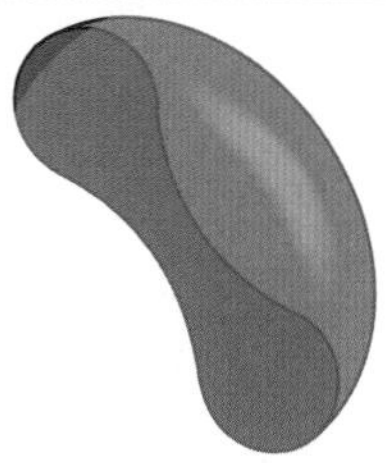

b) The cytoplasm of red cells contains haemoglobin.

What does haemoglobin do? ....

c) Red cells in humans and most other mammals have no nucleus. Suggest a reason why.

....

Section Three — Human Biology Part One

Questions on Lungs and Breathing

Q1   In the sentences below circle the correct words in the <u>underlined</u> pairs.

a) The breathing system takes <u>air</u> / <u>oxygen</u> into and out of the body.

b) This allows <u>carbon dioxide</u> / <u>oxygen</u> to pass from the air into the bloodstream.

c) It also allows <u>carbon dioxide</u> / <u>oxygen</u> to pass out of the bloodstream into the air.

Q2   The diagram shows the *thorax*.
Match up the parts
with the correct labels.

Some parts will have
more than one label.

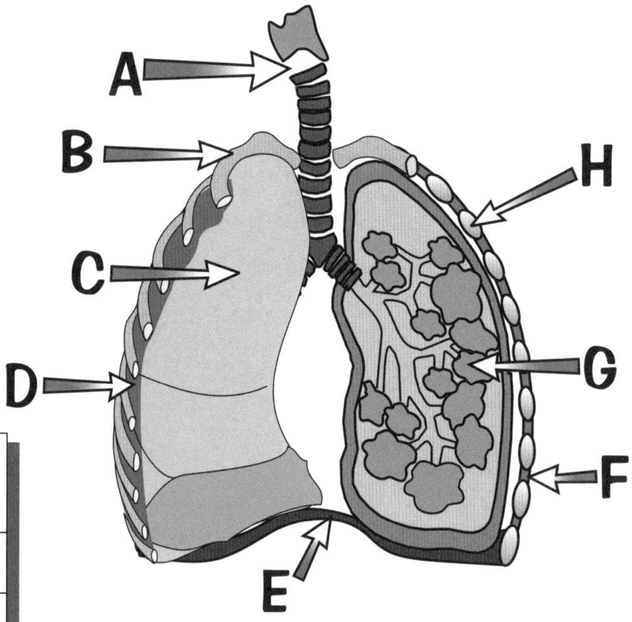

Name of part	label
alveoli	
diaphragm	
intercostal muscles	
lung	
ribs	
trachea	

Q3   *When air is breathed in through the nose or mouth, it passes through parts of the breathing system to the <u>alveoli</u>.*

Write down these parts of the breathing system in the correct order, starting at the nose:

| bronchioles | trachea | bronchi | alveoli |

Nose ⟹ .... ⟹ ....

.... ⟸ ....

Questions on Lungs and Breathing

Q4   Match the part of the breathing system to its correct function.

| Name of Part | | Function |

the ribcage

the diaphragm

the thorax

separates the lungs from the lower part of the body

is the upper part of the body containing the lungs

protects the lungs from damage

Q5   Complete the paragraph below using the words given.

oxygen	carbon dioxide	alveoli	alveolus	red

Each lung contains millions of tiny air sacs called .... The alveoli

are surrounded by a network of blood capillaries. At each .... ,

.... passes into the blood and .... passes out of

the blood. .... blood cells carry the oxygen to all the cells in the body.

Q6 a) The *trachea* has rings of cartilage around it. What do these rings of cartilage do?

....

....

b) The trachea splits into smaller air passages called *bronchi*.
How many bronchi do each of us have?

Number of bronchi   ....

c) What is a bronchiole?

....

d) What are the alveoli?

....

Questions on Lungs and Breathing

Q7 *The air we breath out has a different composition to the air we breath in.*

Gas	% in inhaled air	% in exhaled air
oxygen		
carbon dioxide		
nitrogen		

Complete the table above to show the percentages of oxygen, carbon dioxide and nitrogen in inhaled and exhaled air. Use the numbers from the box below.

0.04	21	78	16	5	78

Q8 The left hand side of the table below explains what happens when we breathe in.

Complete the right hand side of the table to explain what happens when we breathe out.

Use these words:

more	downwards	relax	decreases	up	relax	out

Breathing In	Breathing Out
The diaphragm muscles contract.	The diaphragm muscles _____.
This causes the diaphragm to flatten.	This causes the diaphragm to move upwards.
The muscles between the ribs contract.	The muscles between the ribs _____.
This pulls the ribcage upwards.	This pulls the ribcage _____.
The volume of the thorax increases.	The volume of the thorax _____.
The pressure inside the thorax goes down.	The pressure inside the thorax goes _____.
The pressure inside the thorax gets less than atmospheric pressure.	The pressure inside the thorax gets _____ than atmospheric pressure.
Air is pushed into the lungs from outside to make the pressures equal.	Air is pushed _____ of the lungs to make the pressures equal.

Q9 Circle the correct words from the underlined pairs in the sentences below.

Gaseous exchange happens in the trachea / alveoli.

The cilia keep the lungs clean / warm.

The mucous membranes make the air coming into the air passages dry / moist and warm / cold.

<u>Questions on Respiration</u>

Q1 Complete the sentences below about respiration using the words from this list:

molecules	all	large	temperature	smaller	contract	plants

Respiration is a process that takes place in .... living cells. Respiration

transfers energy from food .... in animals and .... The

energy from respiration is used to make .... molecules from ....

ones, to let muscles ...., and to keep a constant body ....

Q2 a) Put a tick in the box ☐ next to each correct sentence about respiration:

☐ Plants cannot respire.

☐ Respiration means getting air in and out of the lungs.

☐ Respiration releases energy from food molecules in cells.

b) Write down the correct versions of the sentences above that are wrong.

....

....

Q3 a) Complete the following word equation to describe respiration.

Glucose + ... $\longrightarrow$ .... + water (+ energy).

b) Look at your equation. What two substances are needed for respiration?

Substance 1 ....

Substance 2 ....

c) What two substances are produced by respiration?

Substance 1 ....

Substance 2 ....

Questions on Anaerobic Respiration

Q1 The word equation for *aerobic* respiration is:

glucose + oxygen $\Longrightarrow$ carbon dioxide + water (+ energy transferred)

In *anaerobic* respiration in humans, energy is released by converting glucose into lactic acid. No oxygen is needed for this to happen.

a) Write the word equation for anaerobic respiration in humans:

.... $\Longrightarrow$ .... + ...

b) Aerobic respiration releases 16,000 J from 1g of glucose, and anaerobic respiration releases 833 J from 1g of glucose. Which process releases the most energy from glucose?

....

c) Write down one similarity, and one difference between aerobic and anaerobic respiration.

Similarity ....

Difference ....

d) Why are the two types of respiration named aerobic and anaerobic?

....

....

Q2 Complete the sentences below about anaerobic respiration using the words from this list:

cramp	energy	shortage	oxygen
lactic acid		poison	respiring

Anaerobic respiration in humans produces .... from glucose without

needing .... This means that when there is a .... of oxygen, cells

can carry on .... for a short time.

Anaerobic respiration releases .... as a waste. This is a mild ....

and can cause ....

Section Three — Human Biology Part One

Questions on Anaerobic Respiration

Q3 *David does a simple experiment to investigate respiration and muscle activity.*

He rapidly clenches and unclenches his fist, counting how many times he can do this before his hand feels like it's going to fall off. His results are shown in the table on the right.

Number of clenches	
hand lowered	hand raised
201	82

Circle the correct words in each of the <u>underlined</u> pairs in the sentences below:

a) At the start of the experiment, <u>aerobic</u> / <u>anaerobic</u> respiration was happening in his muscles.

b) At the end of the experiment, <u>aerobic</u> / <u>anaerobic</u> respiration was happening in his muscles.

c) During the experiment, <u>lactic acid</u> / <u>carbon dioxide</u> was made which caused cramp.

d) Why does it make a difference whether his hand is raised or lowered during the experiment?

....

....

Q4 The word equation for fermentation is:

glucose ⟹ alcohol + carbon dioxide (+ energy transferred).

Circle the correct words in each of the <u>underlined</u> pairs in the sentences below:

a) Fermentation is an example of <u>aerobic</u> / <u>anaerobic</u> respiration.

b) Yeast is a microscopic <u>bacterium</u> / <u>fungus</u> that can produce <u>oxygen</u> / <u>carbon dioxide</u> and <u>water</u> / <u>alcohol</u> from glucose by fermentation.

Questions on Anaerobic Respiration

Q5 Kathryn has entered a running race. The graph opposite shows the amount of _lactic acid_ in her blood and her rate of oxygen uptake during the race.

The race takes place between the times marked A and B on the graph.

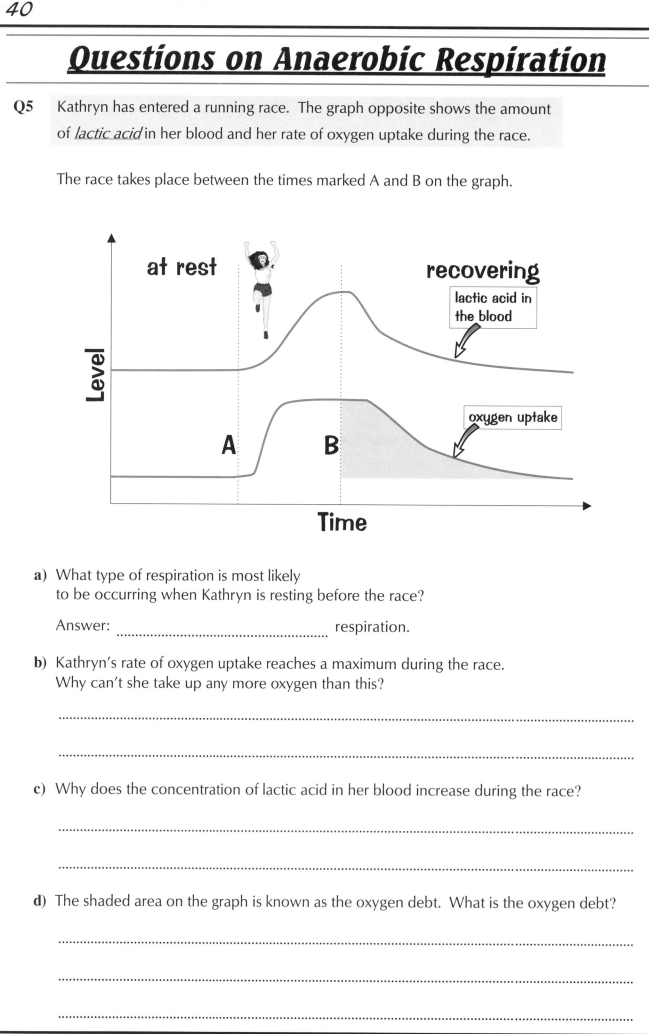

a) What type of respiration is most likely to be occurring when Kathryn is resting before the race?

Answer: .... respiration.

b) Kathryn's rate of oxygen uptake reaches a maximum during the race. Why can't she take up any more oxygen than this?

....

....

c) Why does the concentration of lactic acid in her blood increase during the race?

....

....

d) The shaded area on the graph is known as the oxygen debt. What is the oxygen debt?

....

....

....

Questions on The Nervous System

Q1 a) Put a tick in the box next to each correct sentence about the nervous system:

☐ Receptors are cells which can detect changes in the environment.
☐ A stimulus is a change in the environment.
☐ There are receptors in the ear which are sensitive to changes in position.
☐ Nerve impulses pass from the brain to the receptors.

b) The sentence without a tick is incorrect. Write down a correct version of it in the space below.

....

Q2 Match up the following sense organs with the receptors they contain.

| Organs | ⟹ | Receptors |

eyes have receptors

ears have receptors

tongue and nose have receptors

skin have receptors

that are sensitive to pressure and temperature

that are sensitive to light

that are sensitive to chemicals

that are sensitive to sound and changes in position

Q3 Complete the sentences below using the words from this list:

| see | skin | pressure | taste | nose | hear | balance |

The eye is the organ which allows us to .... The .... is the

organ which gives us the sense of touch by responding to changes in ....

The tongue gives us the sense of .... and the ....

allows us to smell things. The ears are important because they allow us to ....

and keep our ....

Q4 The diagram on the right shows the main features of the nervous system.

a) Name the parts of the nervous system labelled **X**, **Y** and **Z**.

X : ....   Y: ....

Z: ....

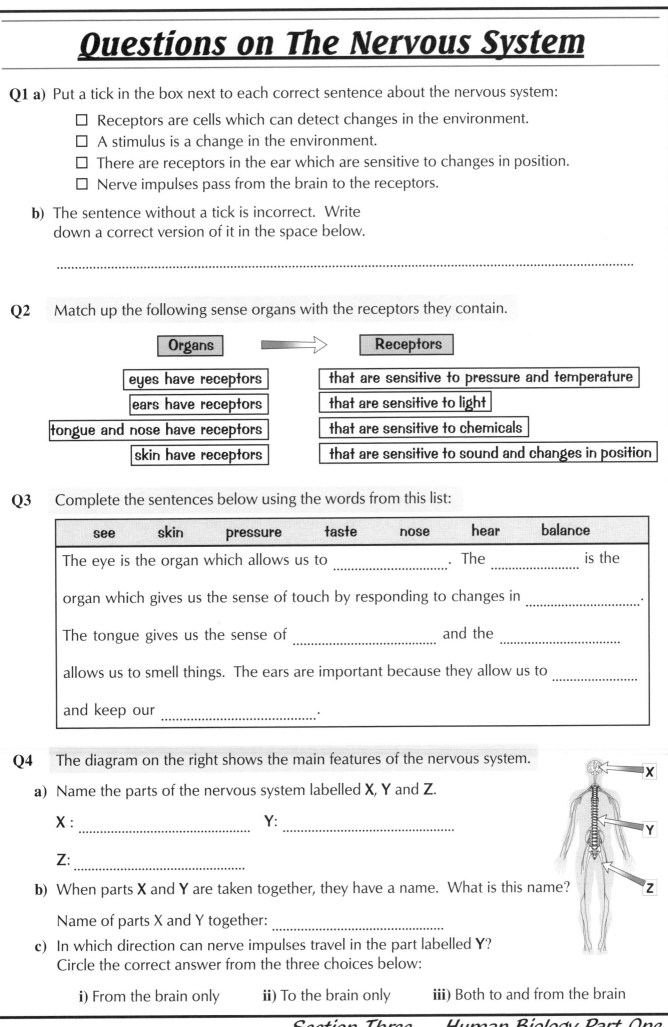

b) When parts **X** and **Y** are taken together, they have a name. What is this name?

Name of parts X and Y together: ....

c) In which direction can nerve impulses travel in the part labelled **Y**?
Circle the correct answer from the three choices below:

i) From the brain only   **ii)** To the brain only   **iii)** Both to and from the brain

Section Three — Human Biology Part One

Questions on The Nervous System

Q5 *When some grit gets in your eye, your eye begins to water. This is a reflex action. The grit irritates the eye, and is the stimulus. The eyes watering is the response.*

   a) Write down another example of a reflex action.

....

   b) Name the stimulus, and the response, in this reflex action.

Stimulus .... Response ....

Q6 Circle the correct words from each underlined pair in the sentences below:

A reflex action is <u>a conscious</u> / <u>an automatic</u> response. It is a response to a <u>stimulus</u> / <u>receptor</u>.

Reflex actions happen very <u>quickly</u> / <u>slowly</u>. They <u>involve</u> / <u>do not involve</u> the <u>brain</u> / <u>Brian</u>.

Reflex actions are <u>considered</u> / <u>emergency</u> reactions.

Q9 Complete these sentences about neurones.

Choose from the list of words below. You can use words more than once, if you need to.

receptor	effector	spinal cord

   a) Sensory neurones carry nerve impulses from the .... to the ....

   b) Motor neurones carry nerve impulses from the .... to the ....

Q10 *The spinal cord can be damaged from an accident or an illness. As a result, the person may be unable to feel anything below the damaged part of the spinal cord.*

Explain why this happens.

....

....

....

Questions on The Eye

Q1 *Look at the diagram below. It shows a section through an eye.*
— Label the different parts A to K, in the spaces provided.

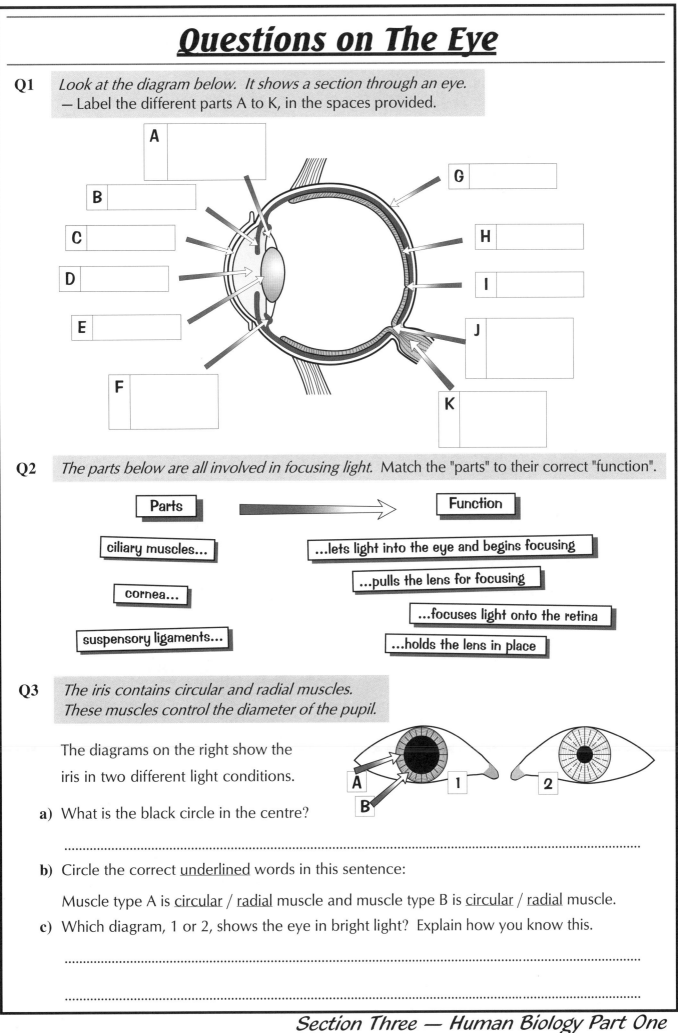

A

B

C

D

E

F

G

H

I

J

K

Q2 *The parts below are all involved in focusing light. Match the "parts" to their correct "function".*

Parts → Function

ciliary muscles...

cornea...

suspensory ligaments...

...lets light into the eye and begins focusing

...pulls the lens for focusing

...focuses light onto the retina

...holds the lens in place

Q3 *The iris contains circular and radial muscles.*
These muscles control the diameter of the pupil.

The diagrams on the right show the iris in two different light conditions.

a) What is the black circle in the centre?

....

b) Circle the correct underlined words in this sentence:

Muscle type A is circular / radial muscle and muscle type B is circular / radial muscle.

c) Which diagram, 1 or 2, shows the eye in bright light? Explain how you know this.

....

....

Questions on the Use of Hormones

Q1 Complete the diagram below to show how hormones travel from a gland, causing a response in a target organ.

Choose from the list of words below:

| endocrine gland | hormone | bloodstream | response | target organ |

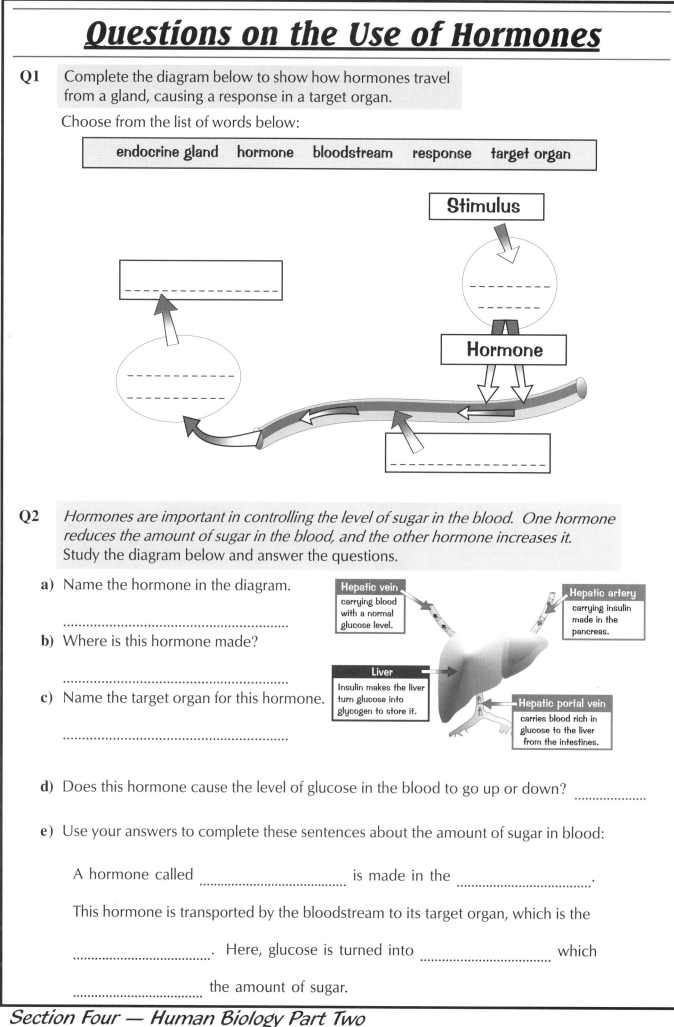

Stimulus

_ _ _ _ _ _ _
_ _ _ _ _ _

Hormone

_ _ _ _ _ _ _ _ _
_ _ _ _ _ _ _ _ _

_ _ _ _ _ _ _ _ _ _ _ _ _ _ _

_ _ _ _ _ _ _ _ _ _ _ _ _ _ _ _

Q2 *Hormones are important in controlling the level of sugar in the blood. One hormone reduces the amount of sugar in the blood, and the other hormone increases it.* Study the diagram below and answer the questions.

a) Name the hormone in the diagram.

....

b) Where is this hormone made?

....

c) Name the target organ for this hormone.

....

Hepatic vein
carrying blood with a normal glucose level.

Hepatic artery
carrying insulin made in the pancreas.

Liver
Insulin makes the liver turn glucose into glycogen to store it.

Hepatic portal vein
carries blood rich in glucose to the liver from the intestines.

d) Does this hormone cause the level of glucose in the blood to go up or down? ....

e) Use your answers to complete these sentences about the amount of sugar in blood:

A hormone called .... is made in the ....

This hormone is transported by the bloodstream to its target organ, which is the

.... Here, glucose is turned into .... which

.... the amount of sugar.

Questions on the Use of Hormones

Q3 Complete the sentences below about hormones using the words from this list:

target	glands	processes	bloodstream	co-ordinated	chemicals

Many .... in the body are ....

by hormones.

Hormones are .... They are produced

by ....

Hormones are transported to their .... organs by the

....

Q4 *Diabetes is a disease in which the pancreas does not produce enough insulin.*

a) What will happen to the level of sugar in the blood if enough insulin is not produced?

....

....

b) Why do people with diabetes need to pay careful attention to their diet?

....

....

c) *Diabetes can be treated by injecting insulin into the bloodstream.* What will this do?

....

....

Questions on Hormones and Fertility

Q1 *The lining of a woman's uterus changes in thickness in a monthly cycle, ready to receive an egg.*

a) What is this monthly cycle called? ....

The diagram on the right shows these changes in thickness during a 28 day cycle. Study the diagram, then answer these questions:

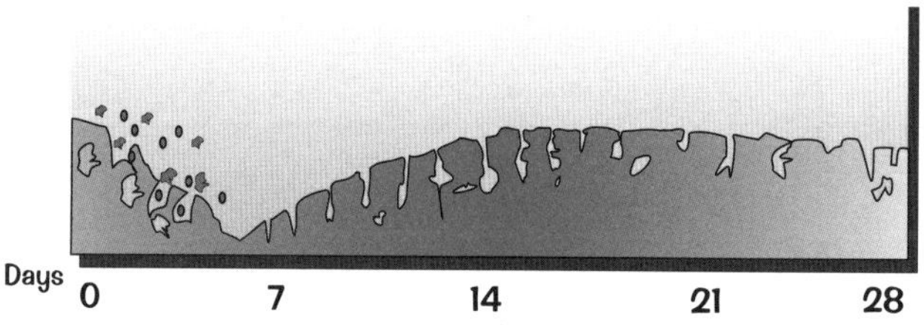

Days 0   7   14   21   28

b) When is the lining of the uterus thickest?

Between day .... and day ....

c) An egg is released from the ovary on day 14. Suggest an advantage of releasing an egg then.

....

....

d) Circle the correct name for the monthly loss of blood: **ovulation/menstruation/micrition**.

Q2 Match the descriptions below to the correct term. One has been done for you.

Description **Term**

Eggs are released from the organs called ● ● menstruation

The hormone that controls the uterus lining thickness is made in ●

The monthly loss of the uterus lining is called ● ● ovulation

The monthly release of an egg is called ● ● the ovaries

Q3 Name a place where hormones are made that control the female reproductive system.

....

Q4 Write down two events in the menstrual cycle that are controlled by hormones.

a) ....   **b)** ....

Q5 *Women's fertility can be controlled using manufactured hormones.*
Circle the correct word in each of the underlined pairs in the sentences below:

a) A woman's fertility <u>increases</u> / <u>decreases</u> if she is given hormones that stimulate egg release.

b) A woman's fertility <u>increases</u> / <u>decreases</u> if she is given hormones that prevent egg release.

Questions on Hormones and Fertility

Q6 Write down one advantage of using manufactured hormones to control fertility in women, and one disadvantage of doing this.

Advantage: ....

....

Disadvantage: ....

....

Q7 Solve the Hormones Wordsearch.

Words to find:

bloodstream	chemicals	endocrine	gland	glucagon
hormone	insulin	liver	oestrogen	
ovaries	pancreas	pituitary	testosterone	uterus

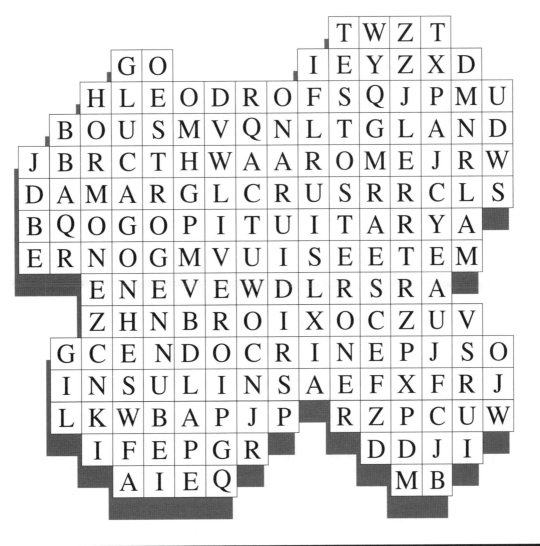

Questions on Disease in Humans

Q1 *The two main types of microbes that can cause disease are bacteria and viruses.*
Write down the name of each type of microbe shown in the pictures b.
(the pictures are not drawn to scale).

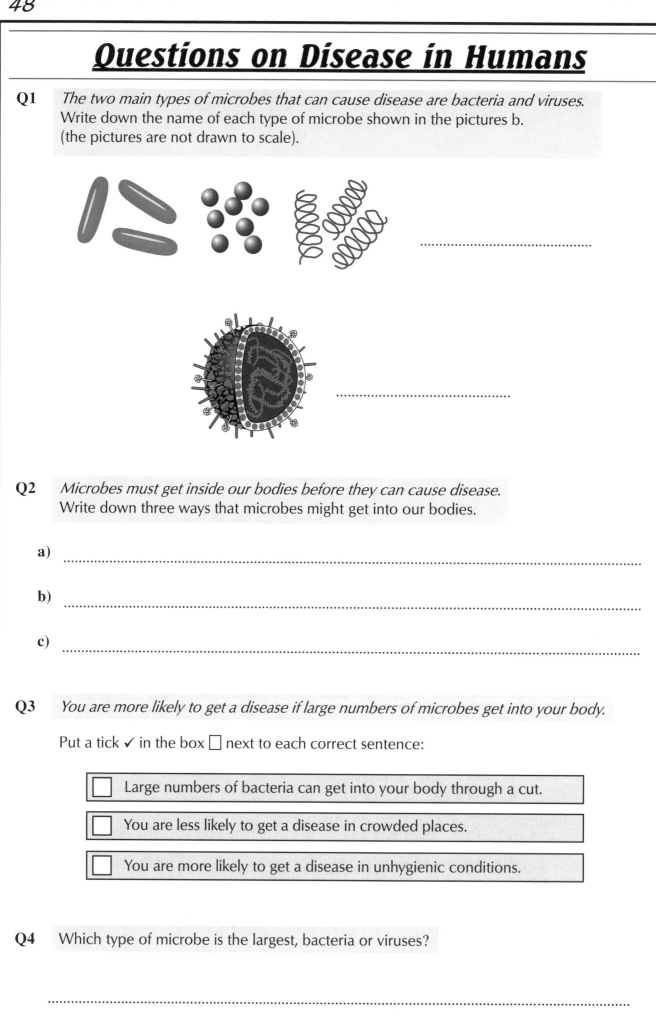

....

....

Q2 *Microbes must get inside our bodies before they can cause disease.*
Write down three ways that microbes might get into our bodies.

a) ....

b) ....

c) ....

Q3 *You are more likely to get a disease if large numbers of microbes get into your body.*

Put a tick ✓ in the box ☐ next to each correct sentence:

☐ Large numbers of bacteria can get into your body through a cut.

☐ You are less likely to get a disease in crowded places.

☐ You are more likely to get a disease in unhygienic conditions.

Q4 Which type of microbe is the largest, bacteria or viruses?

....

Questions on Disease in Humans

Q5   Write down two ways in which bacteria or viruses can be passed from one person to another.

a) ....

....

b) ....

....

Q6   *When bacteria and viruses grow in our bodies, they can produce chemicals called toxins.*
Write down another name for these chemicals.

Name: ....

Q7   *When viruses reproduce in a cell, they break out of the cell in large numbers and infect other*
cells. Circle the correct words from each of the <u>underlined</u> pairs in the sentences below:

Viruses escape from an infected cell through the cell's *nucleus* / *membrane*.

When viruses escape from an infected cell, they *do* / *do not* damage the cell.

Viruses *do* / *do not* need to reproduce inside living cells.

Q8   Complete the sentences below about microbes and disease using the words from this list:

genes   protein   microbes   toxins   rapidly   smaller   nucleus

Diseases can be caused when .... get into the body. Bacteria

and viruses reproduce .... inside the body. They produce

.... which make us feel ill. Viruses are ....

than bacteria, and consist of a .... coat with a few genes inside.

Bacteria have .... but they are not in a ....

Q9   *In Japan, people with a cold often wear a mask over*
their mouth and nose when they go outside.

Suggest a reason why they do this. ....

Questions on Fighting Disease

Q1 *Microbes must get into the body before they can cause disease.*
Our bodies have several natural defences that can stop microbes getting in.

Match the natural defence to the correct part of the body:

natural defence	⟹	part of the body

hydrochloric acid is produced to kill microbes   skin

acts as a barrier to microbes   stomach

a sticky liquid is produced to trap microbes   blood

clots are produced to seal cuts   breathing organs

Q2 *Cells in the blood can defend the body against microbes if they manage to get past the natural defences. The diagrams below show cells that are found in blood. Write down the name of each type of cell in the spaces. Choose from these labels:*

red cell   white cell

....

....

Q3 *White cells help to defend the body against microbes that cause disease.*

What do the red cells do?

....

....

Questions on Fighting Disease

Q5 *At each stage in getting a disease caused by a microbe, the body has defences.*
For each of the stages below, write down an example of the body's defence against microbes:

Bacteria getting into a cut: ....

....

Bacteria producing toxins: ....

....

Bacteria being breathed in: ....

....

Q6 Look at the diagram on the right, then write down below how each of the parts **A** to **D** can protect the body against microbes.

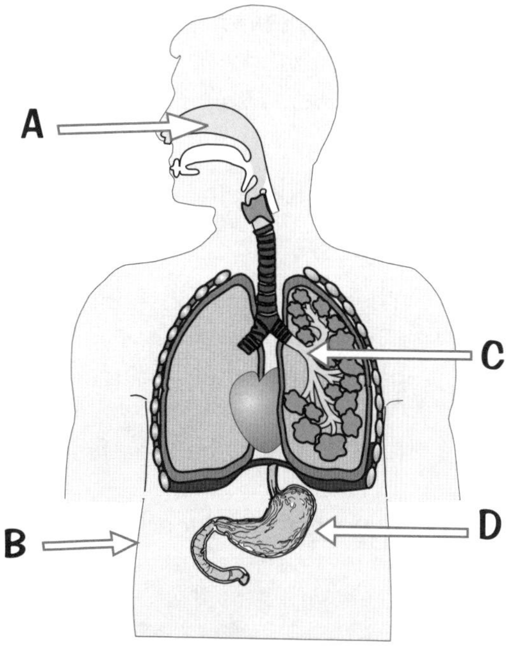

A

A ....

....

B ....

....

C ....

....

D ....

....

Questions on Fighting Disease

Q7 Complete the sentences below using the words from the box:

phagocytes	toxins	ingest	antibodies	antitoxins	microbes

White cells can produce .... which destroy particular

.... They also produce .... which counteract

poisons called .... Special white cells called ....

can .... microbes and so destroy them.

Q8 *In an experiment, somebody was injected with microbes. After 20 days they had produced 1 unit of antibody. After a few months, they were injected again with the same type of microbe. This time, they produced 2.5 units of antibody after 17 days.*

a) Circle the correct words in the underlined pairs in the sentence below:

When you are exposed to a microbe for the

second time, the production of antibodies is

slower / faster than the first time, and more / less

antibody is produced than the first time.

b) *When you are vaccinated against a microbe that causes disease, you are usually injected with dead or damaged microbes, or parts of the microbe.* Explain how vaccinations protect you from microbes that cause disease.

....

....

....

....

....

Questions on Drugs

Q1 a) Match the substances below to the correct descriptions.

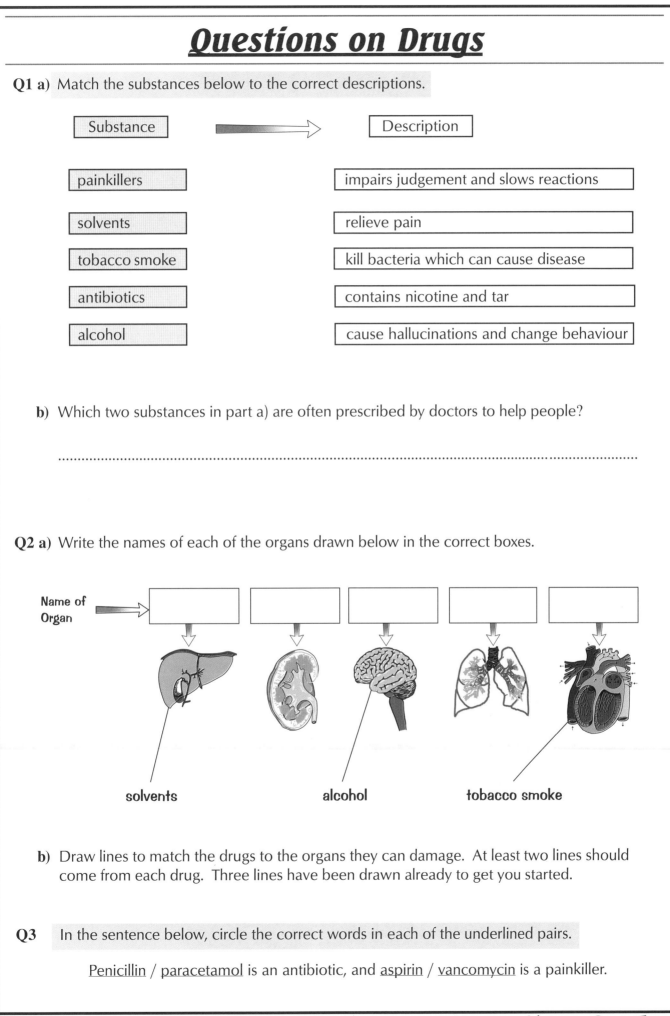

Substance		Description
painkillers		impairs judgement and slows reactions
solvents		relieve pain
tobacco smoke		kill bacteria which can cause disease
antibiotics		contains nicotine and tar
alcohol		cause hallucinations and change behaviour

b) Which two substances in part a) are often prescribed by doctors to help people?

....

Q2 a) Write the names of each of the organs drawn below in the correct boxes.

Name of Organ

solvents   alcohol   tobacco smoke

b) Draw lines to match the drugs to the organs they can damage. At least two lines should come from each drug. Three lines have been drawn already to get you started.

Q3 In the sentence below, circle the correct words in each of the underlined pairs.

Penicillin / paracetamol is an antibiotic, and aspirin / vancomycin is a painkiller.

Questions on Drugs

Q4 Complete the sentences below about drugs using the words from this list:

addicted	processes	chemicals	ill	helpful	withdrawal

Drugs are .... which change the way the body works.

Some are .... to .... people, but

others change the chemical .... in people's bodies.

These changes can make people .... to them and suffer

from .... symptoms if they stop taking the drug.

Q5 a) Put a tick in the box next to each of the correct sentences about alcohol:

☐ Alcohol speeds up reactions and can lead to lack of self-control.

☐ Too much alcohol can lead to unconsciousness and coma.

☐ Alcohol can cause damage to liver and brain cells.

Q6 Study the diagram below, then answer the questions.
One unit of alcohol is 10cm³ of alcohol.

½ pint of beer contains approx. 10cm³ of alcohol = glass of wine = glass of sherry = single measure of spirits

a) How many units are there in ½ pint of beer?

.... Units.

b) How many units are there in a double measure of spirits?

.... Units.

Section Four — Human Biology Part Two

Questions on Drugs

c) *A person at a party drinks a pint of beer, 3 glasses of wine, and two double whiskies (a spirit).* How many units of alcohol has he drunk? Show your working out.

....

....

d) Why would it be unsafe for the person in part c) to drive home after the party?

....

....

Q7 Circle the correct words in each of the underlined pairs in these sentences about tobacco smoke:

1) <u>Tar</u> / <u>nicotine</u> is the substance in tobacco smoke that can cause lung cancer.

2) The substance in tobacco smoke that causes addiction is <u>carbon monoxide</u> / <u>nicotine</u>.

Q8 *The table below shows the effects on the body of three common drugs.*

Complete the table using the words in the box. Some words can be used more than once. Put a tick in the last row if the substance is addictive.

> Liver   Heart   Kidneys   Hallucinations
> Slows reactions   Emphysema   Brain

	alcohol	tobacco	solvents
organs damaged	Brain and	Lungs and	Liver
effect on the body		Lung cancer and	
addictive?			

Questions on Homeostasis

Q1 The graph below shows the results of an experiment into the effects on the body of increasing the air temperature. The squares show the volume of urine produced per hour. The circles show the volume of sweat produced per hour.

a) Circle the correct words in each underlined pair:

As the temperature goes up, the volume of

urine produced goes <u>up</u> / <u>down</u>, and the

volume of sweat produced goes <u>up</u> / <u>down</u>.

b) At which temperature is the volume of urine produced the same as the volume of sweat?

Temperature = ... °C

c) Why do we feel more thirsty in hot weather?

....

....

Q2 Match the method of water loss to the correct organ in the body:

| Method of water loss | ⟹ | Organ |

water is lost by sweating through the   kidneys

water is lost by breathing using the   skin

water is lost as urine made in the   lungs

Q3 In an experiment, 10 members of a class took their temperatures. Their results are shown below:

Body temperature in °C
36.7 36.8 37.1 36.9 36.9 37.0 37.3 36.8 37.2 37.1

a) Work out the average body temperature for these 10 students. Show your working out.

.... °C

b) What is normal human body temperature? .... °C

Section Four — Human Biology Part Two

Questions on Homeostasis

Q4 *For us to stay healthy, the temperature of the body must be maintained at the temperature that enzymes work best. The table below shows how the temperature of a human body and a reptile's body changes during the day in a hot climate.*

Time	4 a.m	8 a.m	12 noon	4 p.m	8 p.m	midnight
Air Temperature (°C)	10	22	39	39	30	8
Human body temperature (°C)	37	37	37	37	37	37
Reptile body temperature (°C)	7	19	10	10	19	7

a) Between which times is the air temperature highest? Between .... and ....

b) The reptile goes underground when the air temperature is highest. Why does it do this?

....

c) What happens to the human's body temperature during the day? ....

d) Circle the correct words in each of the underlined pairs in the sentences below:

1. Reptiles <u>can</u> / <u>cannot</u> use energy from respiration to maintain their body temperature.

2. Humans <u>can</u> / <u>cannot</u> use energy from respiration to maintain their body temperature.

3. Humans maintain their body temperature by sweating when the air temperature gets

   <u>low</u> / <u>high</u>.

Q5 *The amount of sugar in the blood must be kept at a constant level for us to stay healthy.*

a) Name the two hormones involved in keeping the blood sugar level constant.

Hormone 1 .... Hormone 2 ....

b) *In a certain disease, one of these hormones is only produced in small amounts, and the blood sugar level might rise to fatal levels.* Name the disease and the hormone involved.

Name of disease .... Name of hormone ....

Questions on Skin

Q1   *If we get embarrassed or too hot, our skin goes red. This is because the capillaries in the skin get wider and let more blood through.*

Circle the correct words in the <u>underlined</u> pairs in the sentences below about the skin:

a) When the capillaries get wider, this is called <u>vasoconstriction</u> / <u>vasodilation</u>.

b) When we get cold, <u>less</u> / <u>more</u> blood goes through our skin, and our skin looks <u>blue</u> / <u>red</u>.

c) When we get cold, our hairs <u>stand up</u> / <u>lie down</u> to trap a layer of warm air near the skin.

Q2   Complete the flow chart to show how the skin helps us maintain a constant body temperature.   Use the words in the box below.

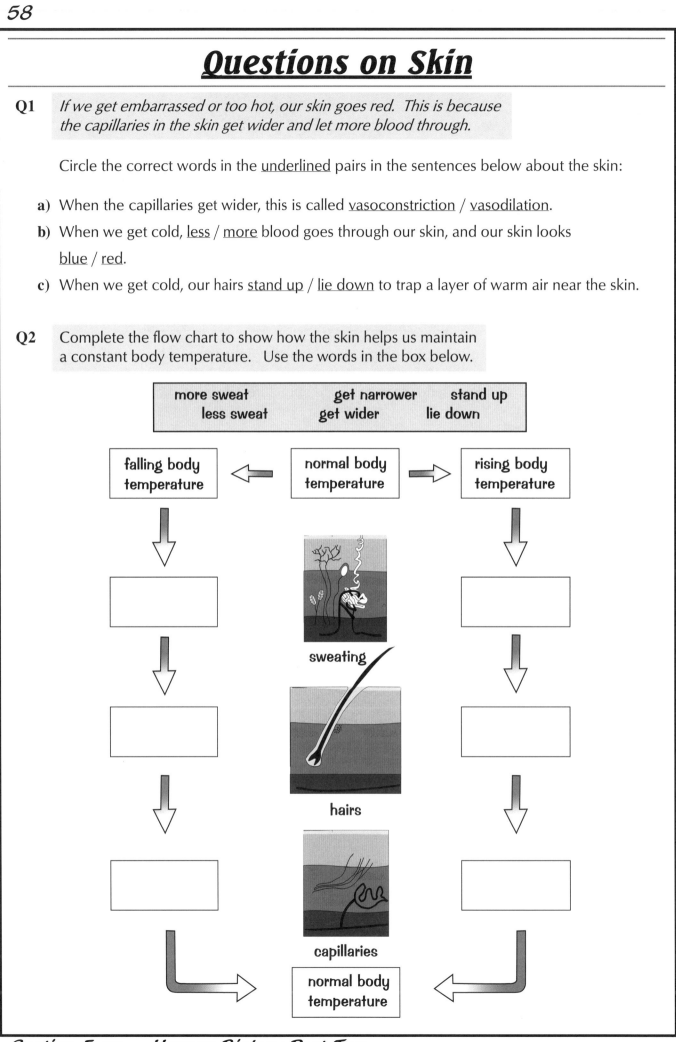

Questions on Skin

Q3 Complete the sentences below about the skin, using the words from the box:

vasoconstriction	lie down	capillaries	hairs	blood	narrower

When the body gets too cold, the .... in our skin get

.... and let less .... through. This is called

.... When we get too hot, the .... on

our skin .... to let heat escape from the skin.

Q4 *The skin is the largest organ of the body. It plays important roles in keeping the body free from disease and protecting our internal organs.*

a) How does the skin protect us from disease?

....

....

b) Why does having waterproof skin protect you from microbes?

....

....

Q5 *We sweat to help maintain a constant body temperature. Sweat contains water and salts.*

a) Put a tick in the box next to each correct sentence:

☐ Water also leaves the body in urine.

☐ Water also leaves the body through the lungs when we breathe in.

☐ Salts also leave the body in urine.

b) *There should be only one box without a tick.* Write down a correct version of this sentence in the space below.

....

....

Questions on Kidneys

Q1 a) Put a tick in the box next to each correct sentence about the excretory system:

| ☐ | The kidneys remove excess water from the bloodstream. |

| ☐ | Urea is produced by the kidneys from the breakdown of excess amino acids. |

| ☐ | Urea is removed by the kidneys, and stored temporarily in urine in the bladder. |

b) *There should be only one box without a tick.* Write down a correct version of this sentence in the space below.

....

Q2 Complete the sentences below about the excretory system using the words from this list:

liver	sweat	bladder	veins	balance	poison
arteries	urine	kidneys	urethra	ions	ureters

The renal .... supply blood to the kidneys, and the renal

.... take blood away from the kidneys. The .... remove

urea from the body. This is a .... that is produced in the

.... is transported from the kidneys to the bladder

through two .... Urine is stored in the .... before

being lost from the body through the ....

The kidneys also remove excess water and .... from the body. These can

be lost in ...., but the kidneys maintain the correct .... of

these substances.

Q3 Suggest two problems that people with damaged kidneys may face.

....

....

....

Questions on Variation

Q1 *Individual animals and plants of the same species are usually not identical. They have different characteristics from each other, and show variation.* Match the **description** to the correct **meaning**:

description	⟹	meaning

individual	differences between single animals or plants of the same kind
species	having the same features
identical	single animal or plant
characteristic	feature, such as appearance
variation	a group of similar living things that can breed with each other

Q2 *There are two types of variation.* — *continuous* variation, and *discontinuous* variation.

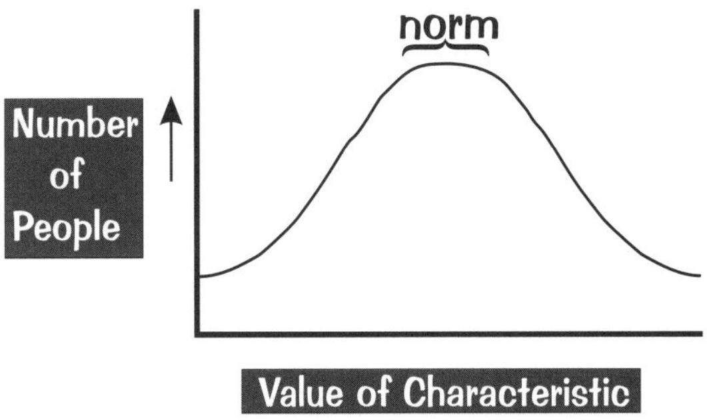

a) Which type of variation is shown in the graph?

....

b) *Some people have earlobes, and some do not. A class surveyed their ears to see how many students had earlobes and how many did not.*

Draw labelled bars in the blank graph on the right to show the sort of results the students might have obtained.

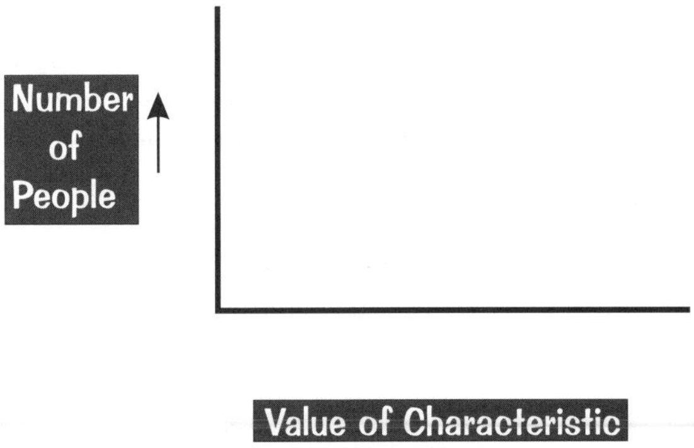

c) Which type of variation is shown by the earlobe survey?

....

Q3 Humans show variation in many of their characteristics. The box below shows six of these characteristics. Three of them show *continuous* variation, and three of them show *discontinuous* variation. Complete the table on the right using these characteristics.

weight
ability to roll tongue
lobed ears
height
intelligence
sex (gender)

continuous variation	discontinuous variation

Questions on Variation

Q4 *People belong to one of four main blood groups, A, B, AB, or O.*

Complete the sentences below about blood groups using the words from this list:

group	discontinuous	categories	four	variation

There are .... main blood groups. The .... in these blood

groups is .... This is because there are distinct .... of

blood ....

Q5 *Animals and plants look similar to their parents because of information passed onto them by their parents. Genes carry this information. Variation between individuals can be due to differences in the genes they have inherited, to differences in the conditions around them, or both.*

Complete the sentences below by circling the correct word in each of the brackets.

Differences in the (**genes / conditions**) produce variation due to genetic causes.

Variation caused by the (**environment / genes**) is due to differences in conditions.

A mixture of genetic and environmental differences (**can / cannot**) cause variation.

Q6 *Identical twins have the same genes and are said to be genetically identical.*

The table below shows the characteristics of four people, code-named M, Q, X, and Z.

Characteristic	M	Q	X	Z
They have a sun tan	✓	✓		
They are male	✓	✓	✓	
They are female				✓
They can roll their tongue	✓		✓	
Natural hair colour is brown	✓	✓	✓	✓
They have bleached white hair			✓	✓
They have brown eyes	✓	✓	✓	

a) Which people are male?

Code-names: ....

b) Who can roll their tongue and has a sun tan? Code-name: ....

c) Which two features are caused by differences in the environment?

1 ....   2 ....

d) Which two people must be the identical twins? Code-names: ....

Questions on Variation

Q7 *When Ayesha looked at the ivy plant growing up the tree in her back garden, she was surprised by how much the size and colour of the leaves varied.*

a) What kind of variation is this, genetic or environmental? ....

b) All mature ivy leaves have the same shape.

Is leaf shape determined genetically or environmentally? ....

c) Is the size of the leaves a continuous or discontinuous variation?

....

Q8 *Azra took geranium cuttings from one of the plants in her garden and gave half of them to her friend Andrew. Each grew their cuttings in their own gardens and a year later compared the growth of the plants and were amazed to see how differently the geraniums had grown.*

The table shows what each set of plants looked like.

	Azra's plants	Andrew's plants
Leaves	Dark green, no spots	Pale green, brown spots
Stems	Tall and thick	Short and thin
Flowers	Large	Short and Thin

a) Suggest two things that could affect the appearance of the geranium plants.

1 ....

2 ....

b) Do you think that the differences in their plants are due to *environmental* variations or

genetic variations? ....

c) Give one reason for your answer to part b).

....

....

....

d) Circle the correct words in each of the brackets to complete the sentences below:

"**All the flowers were orange**" — This is due to (**environmental / genetic**) causes.

"**The flowers were lots of different shades**" — This is (**continuous / discontinuous**) variation.

"**The plants are all of different heights**" — This is (**continuous / discontinuous**) variation
and is due to (**environmental / genetic**) causes.

64

Questions on Genes, Chromosomes and DNA

Q1 *Read the information in the box, then answer the questions.*

> DNA is a chemical found in the nucleus of cells.
>
> DNA is very long, so it is usually folded up into shapes called chromosomes to fit into the nucleus.
>
> A gene is a section of DNA which has the information needed to control a particular characteristic.

a) Where do you find DNA? ....

b) Why is DNA made into chromosomes?

....

c) What do we call a section of DNA that controls a particular characteristic? ....

d) Is the diagram on the right an *animal* cell or a *plant* cell?

....

e) Where in the cell would you find the genes?

....

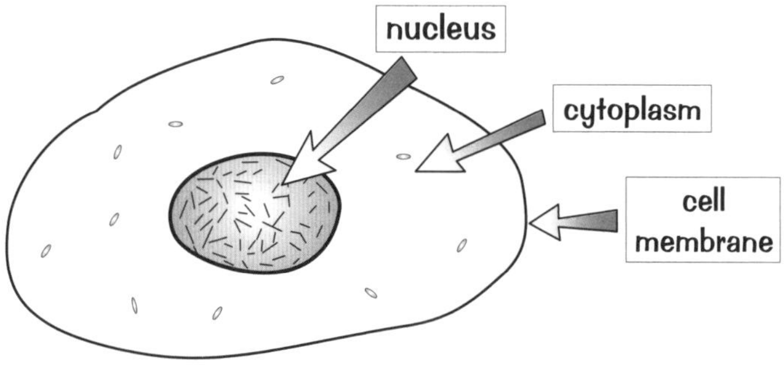

nucleus

cytoplasm

cell membrane

Q2 Put these structures into order, from smallest to largest:

nucleus	gene	chromosome	cell

.... ⟹ .... ⟹ .... ⟹ ....

Smallest .... Largest

Q3 *The diagram on the right shows a typical chromosome.*

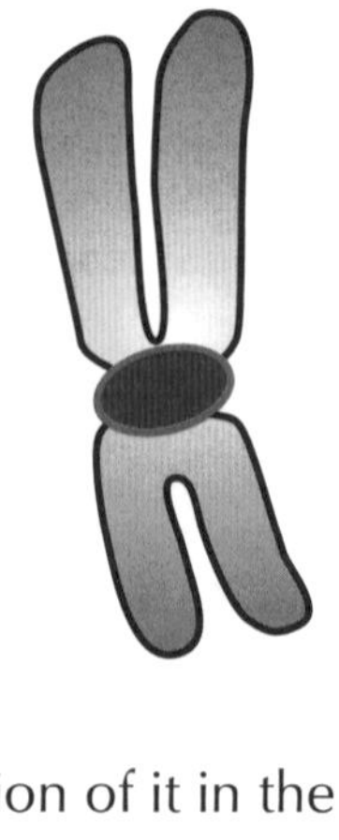

a) Put a tick ✓ in the box ☐ next to each correct sentence about chromosomes:

☐ The name of the chemical in chromosomes is DNA.

☐ Genes contain lots of chromosomes.

☐ Chromosomes are found in the nucleus of the cell.

b) The sentence without a tick is incorrect. Write down a correct version of it in the space below.

....

Section Five — Genetics and Evolution

Questions on Genes, Chromosomes and DNA

Q4 *An experiment was done with two fertilised frog eggs. The eggs came from completely different parents. The nucleus of egg A was put into egg B, and the nucleus of egg B was removed (see the diagram on the right).*

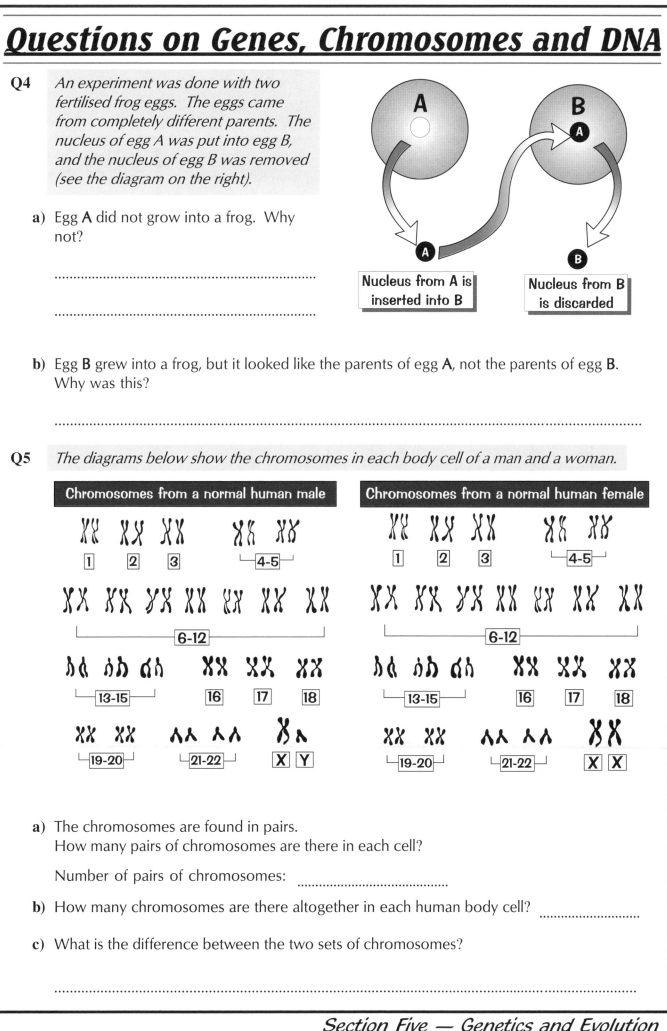

Nucleus from A is inserted into B

Nucleus from B is discarded

a) Egg **A** did not grow into a frog. Why not?

....

....

b) Egg **B** grew into a frog, but it looked like the parents of egg **A**, not the parents of egg **B**. Why was this?

....

Q5 *The diagrams below show the chromosomes in each body cell of a man and a woman.*

a) The chromosomes are found in pairs.
How many pairs of chromosomes are there in each cell?

Number of pairs of chromosomes: ....

b) How many chromosomes are there altogether in each human body cell? ....

c) What is the difference between the two sets of chromosomes?

....

Questions on Asexual Reproduction

Q1 *There are two types of reproduction, asexual reproduction and sexual reproduction. Complete the table below with the sentences in the box to show the differences between asexual and sexual reproduction.*

> Male and female sex cells join.
> Offspring are not genetically identical to parents.
> No joining of cells needed.
> Two parents are needed
> Offspring are genetically identical to parent.
> Only one parent is needed.

Asexual reproduction	Sexual reproduction

Q2 *Genetically identical individuals are called clones. Gardeners can produce clones by taking "cuttings" from one plant. If they are kept in a damp atmosphere or in moist compost, the cuttings eventually grow roots and become a new plant (see diagram).*

Tips are removed and grown in compost

a) Complete the following sentence:

Clones are .... organisms.

b) What type of reproduction is involved in this method?

....

c) Why are the new plants called *clones?*

....

d) Why would a gardener want to take cuttings from a plant that produces prize-winning flowers?

....

Questions on Asexual Reproduction

Q3 *Unlike humans, many plants reproduce asexually.*

a) Give *three* examples of plants which reproduce asexually.

Example 1 ....

Example 2 ....

Example 3 ....

b) For one of the examples above say how the plant actually carries out asexual reproduction.

....

....

Strawberry plants can reproduce in two ways.
They can use flowers, and they can also use runners.

c) Put a tick ✓ in the box ☐ next to each correct
sentence about reproduction in strawberry plants:

☐ Asexual reproduction involves runners.

☐ Flowers are needed for strawberry fruits to form.

☐ Seeds produce new plants that are genetically
identical to each other.

d) The sentence without a tick is incorrect.
Write down a correct version of it in the space below.

....

e) Complete the following passage about asexual reproduction using the words or phrases in
the box below. You can use the word or phrases once, more than once or not at all.

all completely different	two	clones	exactly the same	one

For an organism to reproduce asexually, ... parent is needed. The offspring

produced by this type of reproduction have genes which are ....

.... as the parent. They are said to be .... of each other.

Questions on Sexual Reproduction

Q1 a) Complete the following sentences about sexual reproduction
by circling the correct word in each of the brackets.

Sex cells are called (**gametes / genes**).

Male sex cells are called (**testes / sperm**). Female sex cells are called (**ova / ovaries**).

When sex cells join together this is called (**pollination / fertilisation**). The chromosomes

(**pair up / divide in two**) and a (**foetus / zygote**) is formed.

b) Complete the diagram below to show what the chromosomes are like in the fertilised egg.

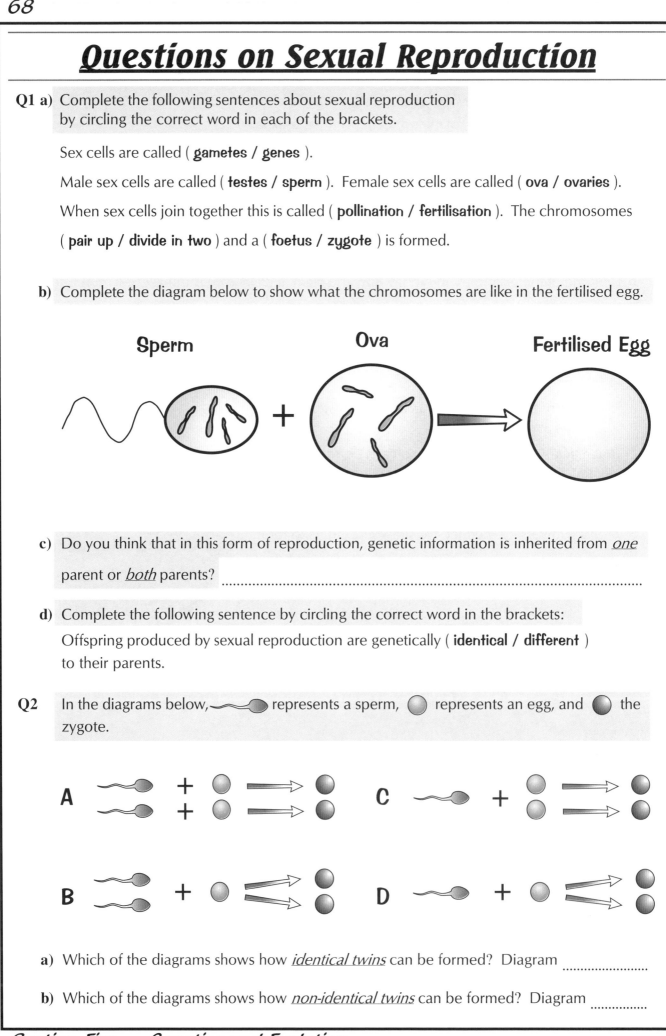

c) Do you think that in this form of reproduction, genetic information is inherited from *one*

parent or *both* parents? ....

d) Complete the following sentence by circling the correct word in the brackets:

Offspring produced by sexual reproduction are genetically (**identical / different**)
to their parents.

Q2 In the diagrams below, ⬱ represents a sperm, ⬯ represents an egg, and ⬮ the
zygote.

a) Which of the diagrams shows how *identical twins* can be formed? Diagram ....

b) Which of the diagrams shows how *non-identical twins* can be formed? Diagram ....

Section Five — Genetics and Evolution

Questions on Reproduction in Humans

Q1 The charts below show what happens in the menstrual cycle when a woman does not become pregnant.

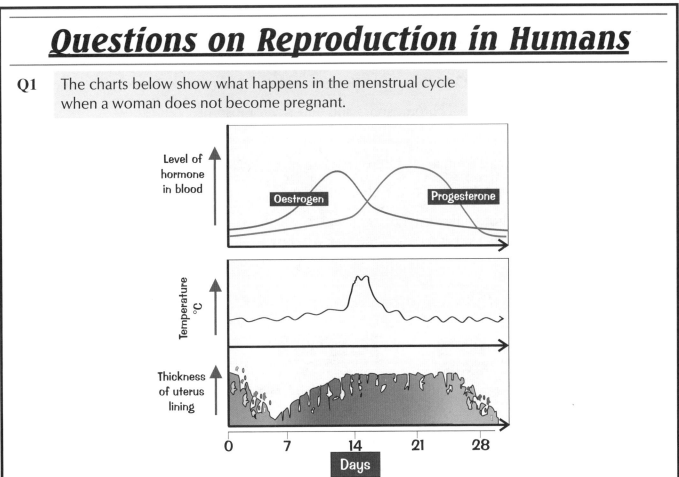

Study the charts, then circle the correct word in each bracket :

a) Between day 0 and day 5, the lining of the uterus (**builds up / breaks down**).

b) When the lining of the uterus breaks down, it is called (**implantation / menstruation**).

c) An egg is released around day 14. Body temperature is (**highest / lowest**) then.

d) As the level of oestrogen increases, the lining of the uterus gets (**thinner / thicker**).

e) After an egg is released, the level of (**oestrogen / progesterone**) reaches a maximum.

f) As the level of progesterone decreases, the lining of the uterus gets (**thinner / thicker**).

Q2 Complete the sentences below about reproduction using the words from the list:

fertilised	breaks	down	ovary	uterus	vagina	oviduct	thicker

A mature egg passes from the .... along the .... to the uterus.

The lining of the .... becomes .... ready to receive the egg if it

is .... If the egg is not fertilised, the lining ....

.... and is lost through the ....

Questions on Inheritance

Q1 a) Put a tick ✓ in the box ☐ next to each correct sentence about inheritance of sex (gender):

☐ Males have one X chromosome and one Y chromosome.

☐ Females have two X chromosomes.

☐ A sperm can contain an X chromosome or a Y chromosome.

☐ An egg can contain only a Y chromosome.

b) The sentence without a tick is incorrect.
Write down a correct version of it in the space below.

....

Q2 *The diagram below shows some of the events leading to the production of a baby.*

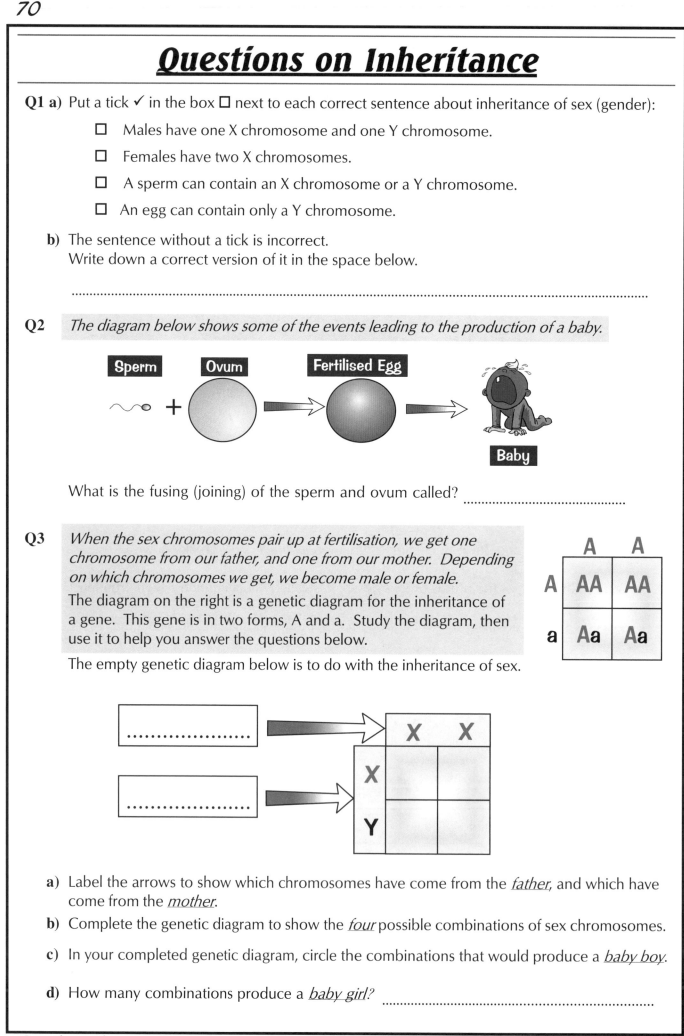

What is the fusing (joining) of the sperm and ovum called? ....

Q3 *When the sex chromosomes pair up at fertilisation, we get one chromosome from our father, and one from our mother. Depending on which chromosomes we get, we become male or female.*

The diagram on the right is a genetic diagram for the inheritance of a gene. This gene is in two forms, A and a. Study the diagram, then use it to help you answer the questions below.

	A	A
A	AA	AA
a	Aa	Aa

The empty genetic diagram below is to do with the inheritance of sex.

a) Label the arrows to show which chromosomes have come from the *father*, and which have come from the *mother*.

b) Complete the genetic diagram to show the *four* possible combinations of sex chromosomes.

c) In your completed genetic diagram, circle the combinations that would produce a *baby boy*.

d) How many combinations produce a *baby girl?* ....

Section Five — Genetics and Evolution

Questions on Inheritance

Q4 a) Fill in the boxes to complete the genetic diagram below showing the inheritance of sex:

chromosomes in parents   **XX**   **XY**

chromosomes in gametes   **X**   □   **X**   □

chromosomes in offspring   **XX**   □   □   □

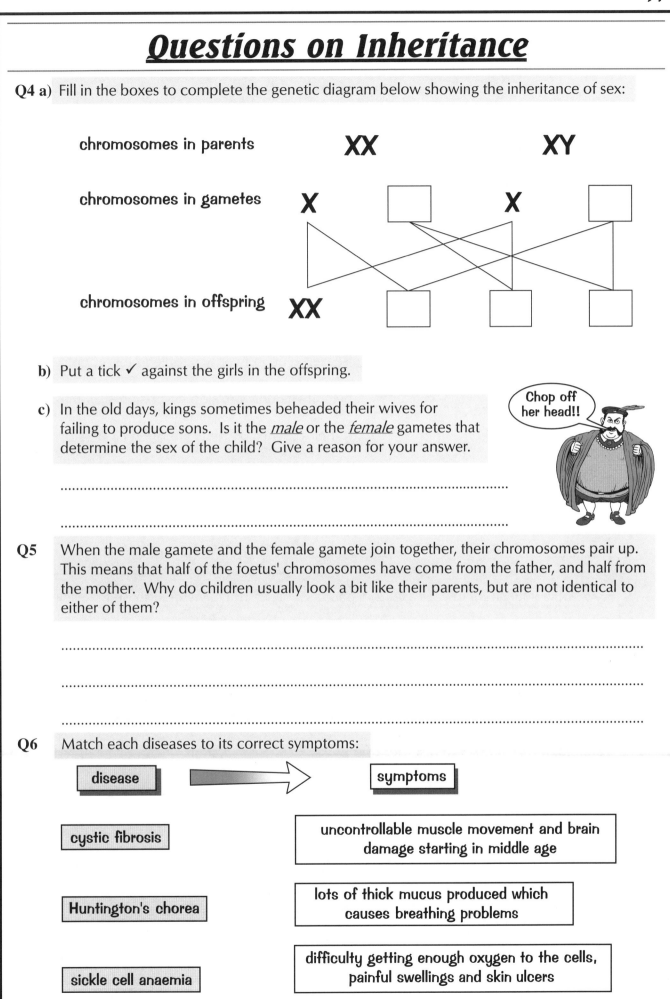

b) Put a tick ✓ against the girls in the offspring.

c) In the old days, kings sometimes beheaded their wives for failing to produce sons. Is it the *male* or the *female* gametes that determine the sex of the child? Give a reason for your answer.

"Chop off her head!!"

....

....

Q5 When the male gamete and the female gamete join together, their chromosomes pair up. This means that half of the foetus' chromosomes have come from the father, and half from the mother. Why do children usually look a bit like their parents, but are not identical to either of them?

....

....

....

Q6 Match each diseases to its correct symptoms:

| disease | ➡ | symptoms |

cystic fibrosis

Huntington's chorea

sickle cell anaemia

uncontrollable muscle movement and brain damage starting in middle age

lots of thick mucus produced which causes breathing problems

difficulty getting enough oxygen to the cells, painful swellings and skin ulcers

Section Five — Genetics and Evolution

Questions on Inheritance

Q7   *Sickle cell anaemia is a disorder of the red blood cells. It must be inherited from both parents. The parents need not have the disease. They can still pass it on without having it themselves if they are both carriers of the disease.*

   a) What is a carrier? ....

   b) Why can being a carrier of the disorder be an *advantage* in countries where there's a lot of malaria?

   ....

Q8 a) Complete the following paragraph about Cystic fibrosis.

chest	mucus	genetic	defective	digestive	both

Cystic fibrosis is a .... disease. One in twenty people in this country

carry the .... gene. A person will only develop cystic fibrosis if they

inherit the gene from .... of their parents. Parents are often carriers of

the disorder without developing cystic fibrosis themselves. Sufferers' membranes

produce thick sticky .... in the lungs and pancreas causing

.... infections and .... problems.

   b) How could you inherit the disease from parents who do not have the disease themselves?

   ....

Q9 a) Complete the following paragraph about Huntington's Chorea

mental	disease	worse	nervous	one

Huntington's Chorea is a disorder of the .... system. It can be inherited

from just .... parent who has the disorder. Symptoms only develop when the

person who has inherited the disorder is over 35-40 years of age. The ....

causes involuntary movements and .... deterioration. There is no cure

and the condition gets progressively ....

   b) How is it possible that a young person has Huntington's Chorea without realising it?

   ....

Questions on Selective Breeding

Q1 *The Large White is a variety of pig often kept by farmers.*
It has been produced by selective breeding from wild boars.

Wild Boar

a) From the pictures, give two features that pig breeders
have selected for when producing the Large White.

Feature 1 ....

Feature 2 ....

Large White Pig

b) Give two features, not seen in pictures, that pig breeders might want to introduce.

1 .... 2 ....

Q2 *People have produced new varieties of dogs to achieve a particular look*
or temperament. All dogs have been bred from wolf ancestors.

Shar-pei   **Basset hound**   **Bedlington**   **Bulldog**

a) Give one feature of wolves that would not be found in varieties of pet dogs.

....

b) Give one feature of wolves that might be found in varieties of guard dogs.

....

c) Write down one feature that dog breeders have selected for when breeding Basset hounds.

....

d) Write down one feature of Basset hounds that you think would cause it problems, and why.

....

Q3 Complete the sentences below about selective breeding using the words from the list:

disease	varieties	animals	flavour	artificial	several	increased	sexual

Selective breeding is also called .... selection and involves ....

reproduction. We use it to produce new .... of animals and plants. It has

been used to produce crop plants and agricultural .... with

.... yield, improved .... and resistance to ....

Selective breeding can take .... generations.

Questions on Mutations

Q1 *Genes can change into new forms. These new forms of genes are called mutations.*

   a) What is a *mutation?* ....

   b) Put a tick ✓ in the box ☐ next to each correct sentence about mutations:

       ☐ Infra-red light can increase the chance of mutations occurring.

       ☐ X-rays can increase the chance of mutations occurring.

       ☐ Gamma radiation from radioactive substances can increase the chance of mutations.

       ☐ Chemicals called mutagens can increase the chance of mutations occurring.

   c) The sentence without a tick is incorrect.
      Write down a correct version of it in the space below.

      ....

Q2 *Mutations can be a chemical change in just one gene, or they can be a major change in one or more chromosomes. The diagram on the right shows part of two fruit flies, and the chromosomes in a cell from each.*

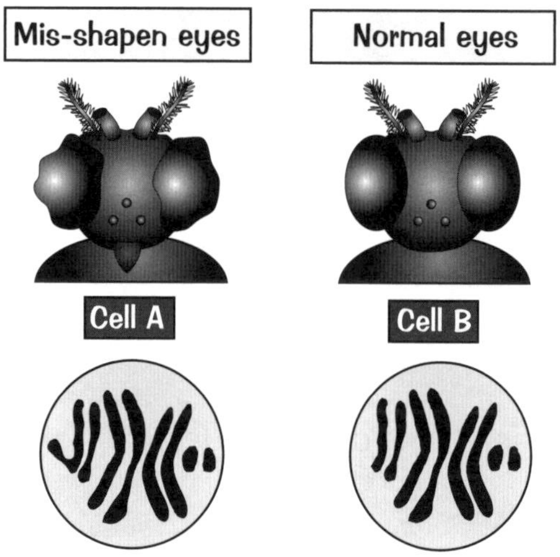

Mis-shapen eyes	Normal eyes
Cell A	Cell B

   a) What is the difference between the chromosomes in *cell A* and the chromosomes in *cell B?*

      ....

      ....

   b) Circle the correct word in the brackets to complete these sentences:

      The mis-shapen eye mutation might have been caused by (**a chemical / an accident**).

      The mutation will be (**caught / inherited**) by the fly's offspring.

Q3 *Cancer can be caused by mutations that cause cells to grow uncontrollably.*

   a) Cigarette smoke contains mutagens. What sort of cancer might they cause? ....

   b) What sort of cancer might too much sunbathing cause? ....

   c) What sort of cancer might chewing tobacco cause? ....

Questions on Mutations

Q4 *Down's Syndrome is a genetic disease caused by a fault in the way the chromosomes separate when the mother's gametes are being formed. People with Down's Syndrome can live very fulfilled lives, but suffer from learning difficulties and a shortened life-span.*

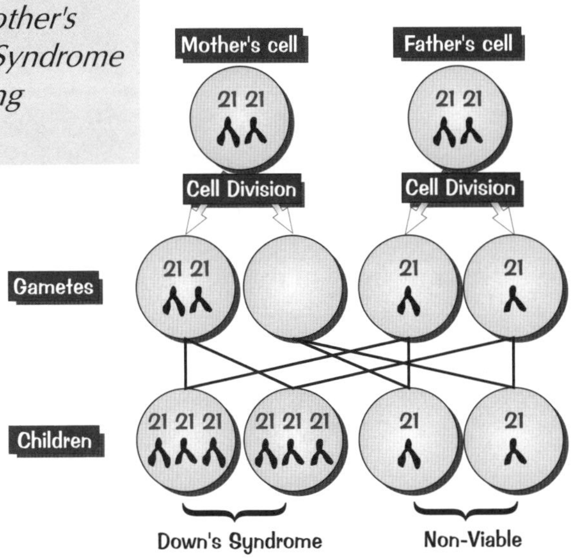

Study the diagram on the right, then answer these questions:

a) Which chromosome is involved? ....

b) If the child receives only one of these chromosomes, is it able to survive to birth?

....

c) Study the table on the right. What happens to the chance of a woman having a Down's Syndrome child as she gets older?

....

....

Mother's age	Chance of having a child with Down's Syndrome
25	1 in 1400
40	1 in 110
45	1 in 30

Q5 *A sheep with very short legs appeared in a farmer's flock in the 18th century. The farmer bred from the sheep and eventually produced a variety of sheep called Ancorn sheep.*

a) Why might a sheep with short legs appear in a normal flock?

....

b) Why would some of the offspring from the sheep also have short legs?

....

c) Suggest an advantage to the farmer of keeping short-legged Ancorn sheep.

....

d) *Most mutations are not an advantage to the animal or plant involved.*
Is having short legs an advantage to the Ancorn sheep? Explain your answer.

....

....

Questions on Fossils and Evolution

Q1 *Fossils are the remains of animals and plants that died many years ago.
Normally when organisms die, they decay.
If the conditions needed for decay are not there, they may be fossilised.*

**Olenellus
(trilobite)**

*The pictures below show three types of fossils. Peat Bog Man was
preserved because there was little oxygen in the water-logged peat,
and the acidic conditions made it difficult for decay bacteria to grow.*

Draw lines to match the insect and the mammoth to the missing conditions for decay.

Peat Bog Man.
Body found in
water-logged
acidic peat.

Insect.
Found in
amber formed
when tree gum
turns solid.

Mammoth.
Found in
an icy
glacier.

oxygen missing   warmth missing   moisture missing

Q2 Complete the sentences below about fossils using the words from this list:

decay	conditions	rocks	animals	minerals	oxygen	hard

Fossils are the remains of plants or .... from many years ago which are found

in .... Many fossils are formed from .... parts which do not

.... easily. These parts are eventually replaced by .... Some fossils

form because one or more of the .... needed for decay are missing. For decay

to happen, ... , moisture, warmth and non-acidic conditions are needed.

Q3 *Species can become extinct if the environment they need to survive
changes, or if new predators, diseases or competitors are introduced.*

a) Dinosaurs are extinct today. How do we know that they once existed at all?

....

b) Write down two things that might have happened to cause the dinosaurs to become
extinct.

1 ....   2 ....

Questions on Fossils and Evolution

Q4 *Life on Earth is thought to be very old, with the first simple living things developing more than three billion years ago. The theory of evolution says that all the species of organisms alive today, and others that are now extinct, evolved from other simpler organisms.*

The horse evolved to its modern appearance over millions of years. Study the diagram on the right, then answer the questions below.

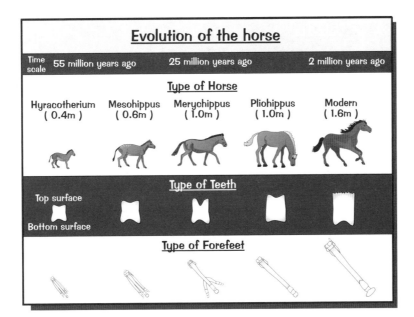

Evolution of the horse

a) How tall was the oldest ancestor of the horse?

Height .... m

b) How do we know what the feet and teeth of these ancestors looked like?

....

c) The earliest teeth were flat with no ridges to cope with soft food.
How have the teeth evolved to cope with tough grasses?

....

d) Modern horses are adapted to run quickly and to see into the distance.
From the evidence in the diagrams, how have horses evolved to do these things?

....

e) What would have happened if the ancestors of the horse had been _unable_ to evolve?

....

f) What causes a feature in living things to change so that this change is passed to their offspring?

....

Questions on Population Sizes

Q1 *The chart on the right shows the change in the numbers of a species of predator and its prey.*

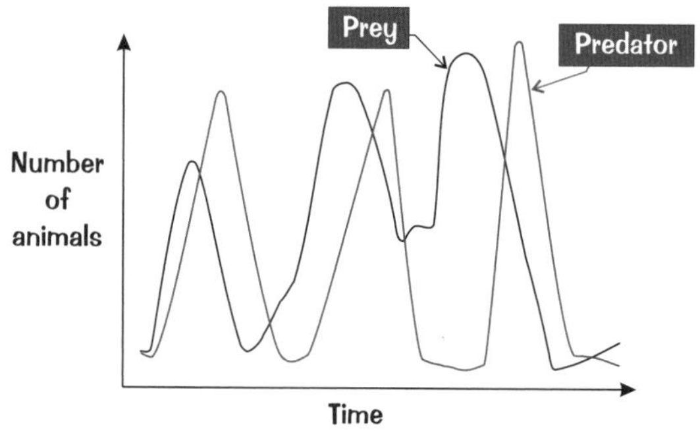

a) Explain what the word predator means.

....

....

b) Explain what the word prey means.

....

c) Give one example of a predator and its prey.

Predator .... Its prey ....

d) Put a tick in the box next to each correct sentence about the graph above:

The number of predators decreases because the number of prey increases.	☐
The number of predators decreases because the number of prey decreases.	☐
If the population of prey increases, more food is available for its predators.	☐
The population is not usually limited by the amount of food available.	☐

e) Look at your answers to part d). The sentences without a tick are incorrect. Write a correct version of each incorrect sentence below.

....

....

Q2 *The number of mice in a wood was estimated at the same time each year for thirteen years.*

The results are shown in the bar chart on the right.

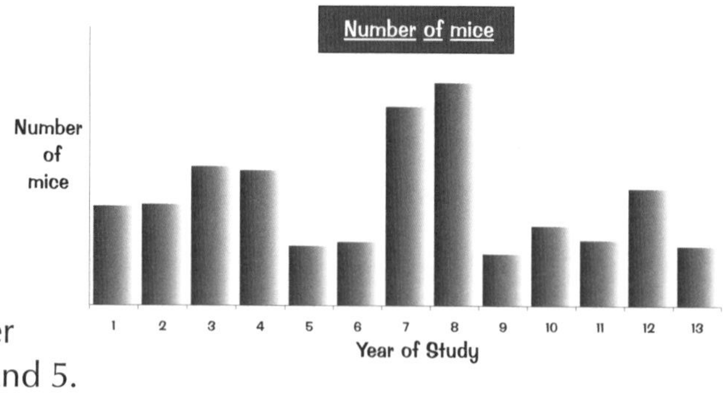

a) Give two possible reasons why the number of mice in the wood fell between years 4 and 5.

....

....

b) Give two possible reasons why the number of mice increased between years 6 and 7, but don't write the opposite of your answers to part a).

....

....

Questions on Populations

Q1 *The graph below shows the average daytime temperature (line) and rainfall (bars) on the northern edge of the Sahara desert.*

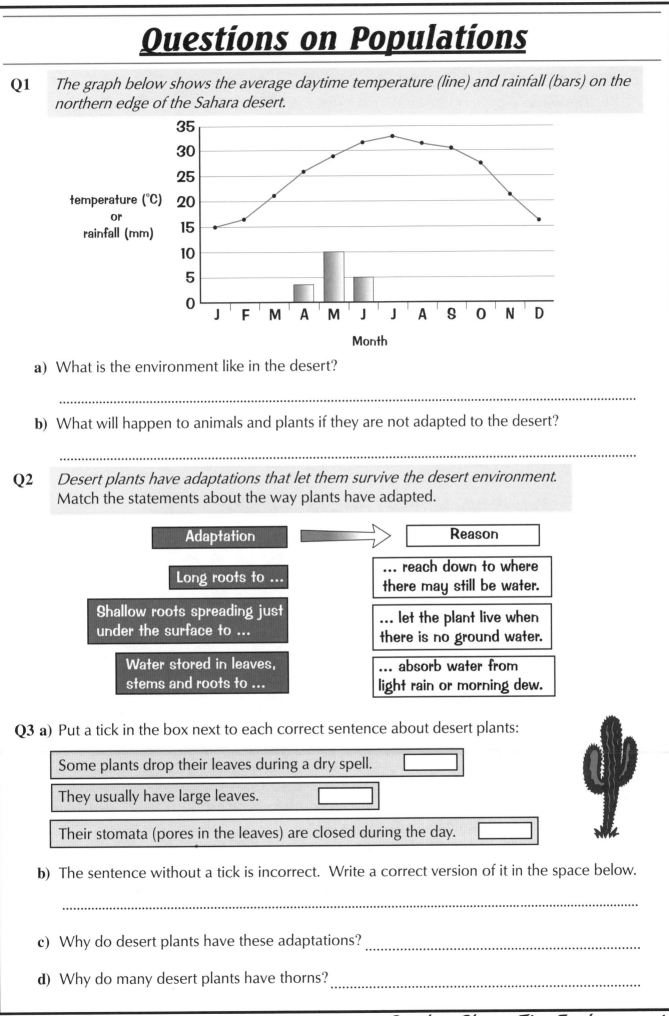

temperature (°C)
or
rainfall (mm)

Month

a) What is the environment like in the desert?

....

b) What will happen to animals and plants if they are not adapted to the desert?

....

Q2 *Desert plants have adaptations that let them survive the desert environment.
Match the statements about the way plants have adapted.*

| Adaptation | ⟹ | Reason |

Long roots to ...

Shallow roots spreading just under the surface to ...

Water stored in leaves, stems and roots to ...

... reach down to where there may still be water.

... let the plant live when there is no ground water.

... absorb water from light rain or morning dew.

Q3 a) Put a tick in the box next to each correct sentence about desert plants:

Some plants drop their leaves during a dry spell. ☐

They usually have large leaves. ☐

Their stomata (pores in the leaves) are closed during the day. ☐

b) The sentence without a tick is incorrect. Write a correct version of it in the space below.

....

c) Why do desert plants have these adaptations? ....

d) Why do many desert plants have thorns? ....

Section Six — The Environment

Questions on Populations

Q4 *The sidewinder adder lives in deserts. It moves sideways across the sand by throwing its body into a series of S-shapes, always keeping a loop off the ground, with two other parts touching.*
Why does it do this?

....

....

Q5 *Many desert animals, such as the kangaroo rat, spend the day in a burrow and come out only at night.*

a) Write down two advantages of doing this.

Advantage 1 ....

Advantage 2 ....

b) Write down a disadvantage of doing this.

....

Q6 *Camels are probably the best-known animals in the desert.*

a) Describe the features that the camels have which make them adapted for desert conditions.

....

....

....

b) *It has been discovered that a shaved camel loses nearly twice as much body water as an unshaved camel.* Suggest why losing its hair could cause this difference.

....

c) *Humans need to maintain a fairly constant body temperature, but camels can tolerate a big change in their body temperature.*
Camels can allow the temperature to go from about 34°C to 41°C during the day, and then they cool off during the night. This means that during the day they do not need to use the methods of cooling that humans do.
How is this advantageous to the camel?

....

....

Questions on Populations

Q7 *The graph below shows the average daytime temperature (line) and rainfall (bars) in the Arctic.*

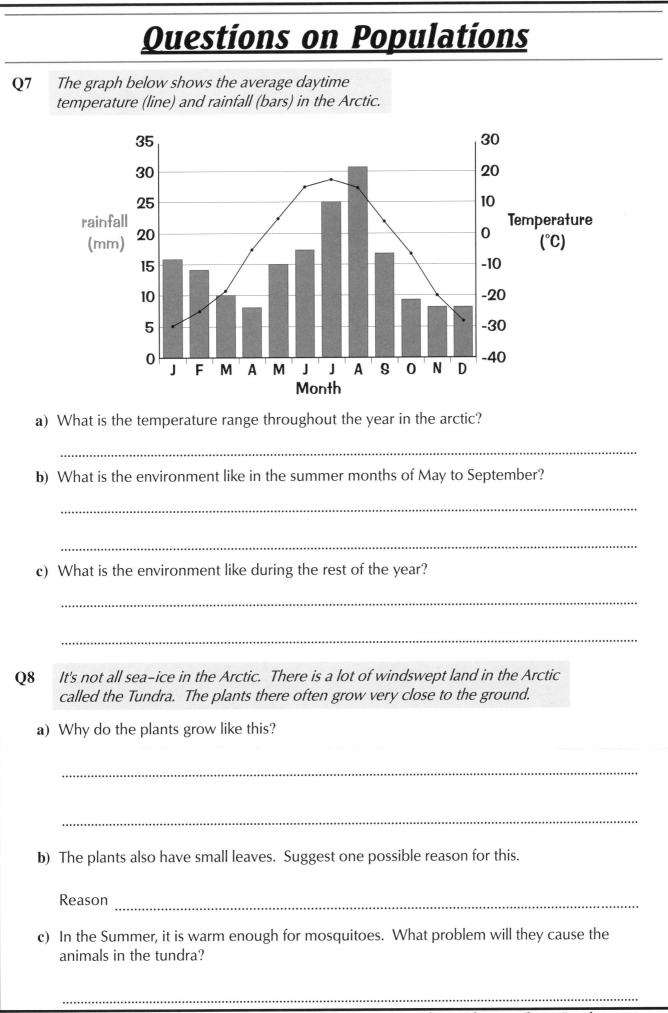

a) What is the temperature range throughout the year in the arctic?

....

b) What is the environment like in the summer months of May to September?

....

....

c) What is the environment like during the rest of the year?

....

....

Q8 *It's not all sea-ice in the Arctic. There is a lot of windswept land in the Arctic called the Tundra. The plants there often grow very close to the ground.*

a) Why do the plants grow like this?

....

....

b) The plants also have small leaves. Suggest one possible reason for this.

Reason ....

c) In the Summer, it is warm enough for mosquitoes. What problem will they cause the animals in the tundra?

....

Questions on Populations

Q9 *Large animals have a small surface area to volume ratio.
This means that they lose heat more slowly than animals
with a large surface area to volume ratio.*

   a) Why do polar bears and walruses have
large bodies with lots of fat?

   ....

   ....

   ....

   b) Lemmings are small rodents that live in the tundra, and have a rounded body about 12cm
long. Why do lemmings live in burrows?

   ....

   ....

   ....

Q10 *Animals have adapted in many ways to allow them to survive their surroundings.*

   a) Why does the snowshoe hare have white fur in the winter and red-brown fur in the
summer?

   ....

   ....

   b) Desert foxes have very large ears, but Arctic foxes only have very small ears.
Suggest a reason for this difference (it is not to do with hearing or hiding).

   ....

   ....

   c) Indian elephants have smaller ears than African elephants. Explain why this adaptation is
important to the elephants living in these countries.

   ....

   ....

Q11 Complete the sentences below using the words from this list:

plants	fat	environments	camouflage	body	insulation	adapted

Animals are .... to different .... They can have different

.... sizes, different amounts of .... and fur for ....

They might also use .... also show adaptations.

Questions on The Greenhouse Effect

Q1 *The temperature on the surface of the Moon ranges from -175°C to 125°C. The average temperature on the surface of the Moon is about -20°C.*

The differences between the Moon's surface temperature and the Earth's surface temperature are because the Earth has an atmosphere. Our atmosphere traps heat by a process known as the greenhouse effect.

Complete the diagram below to show how the greenhouse effect works.

Choose from these labels:

    Earth's surface
    Earth's atmosphere
    Heat from the Sun
    Heat absorbed by the atmosphere

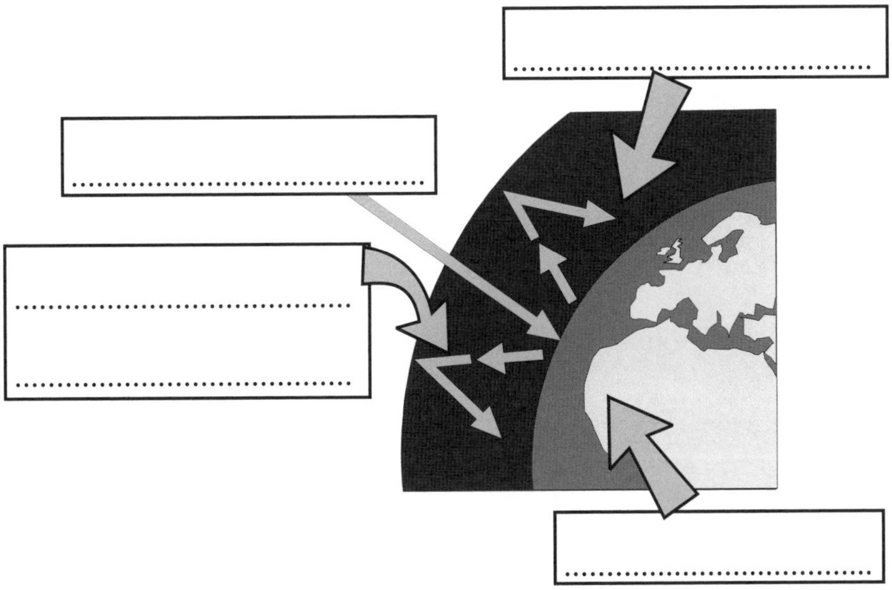

Q2 Complete the paragraph about the greenhouse effect using the correct words from the list:

good	absorbed	surface	Sun	atmosphere	space	warms

Energy from the .... passes through the Earth's .... and

warms the Earth's surface. Heat energy from the Earth's .... is radiated

into .... but some of it is .... by gases in the atmosphere.

This .... the atmosphere, which is .... for life on Earth.

Questions on The Greenhouse Effect

Q3 *Look at the graphs below. They show the amount of carbon released from burning fossil fuels each year since 1850, and the percentage of carbon dioxide in the air each year since 1850.*

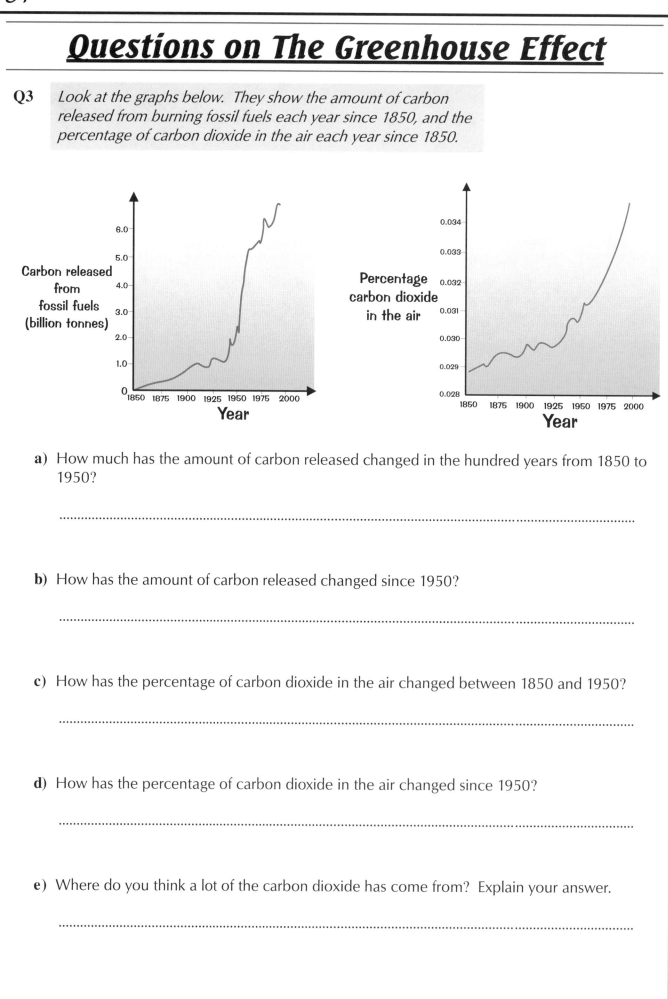

a) How much has the amount of carbon released changed in the hundred years from 1850 to 1950?

....

b) How has the amount of carbon released changed since 1950?

....

c) How has the percentage of carbon dioxide in the air changed between 1850 and 1950?

....

d) How has the percentage of carbon dioxide in the air changed since 1950?

....

e) Where do you think a lot of the carbon dioxide has come from? Explain your answer.

....

Questions on The Greenhouse Effect

Q4 *The graphs below show the changes in average temperatures and sea level since 1880.*

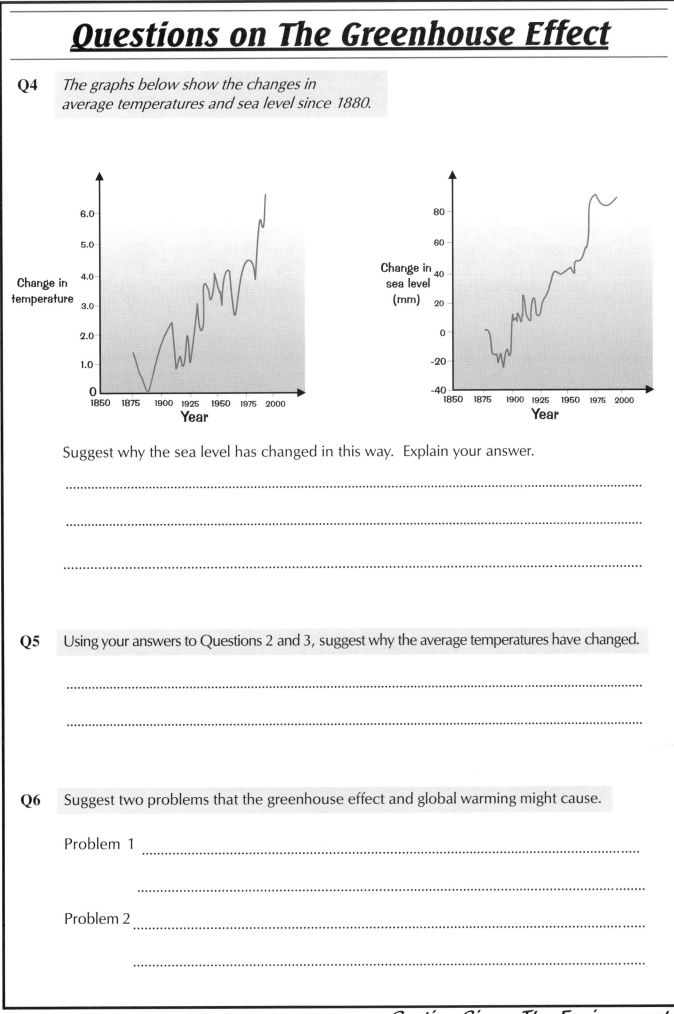

Suggest why the sea level has changed in this way. Explain your answer.

....

....

....

Q5 Using your answers to Questions 2 and 3, suggest why the average temperatures have changed.

....

....

Q6 Suggest two problems that the greenhouse effect and global warming might cause.

Problem 1 ....

....

Problem 2 ....

....

Questions on Acid Rain

Q1   *The table below shows the amount of acid rain gases from different sources.*

The percentage contributions of nitrogen oxides have been plotted on the graph below.

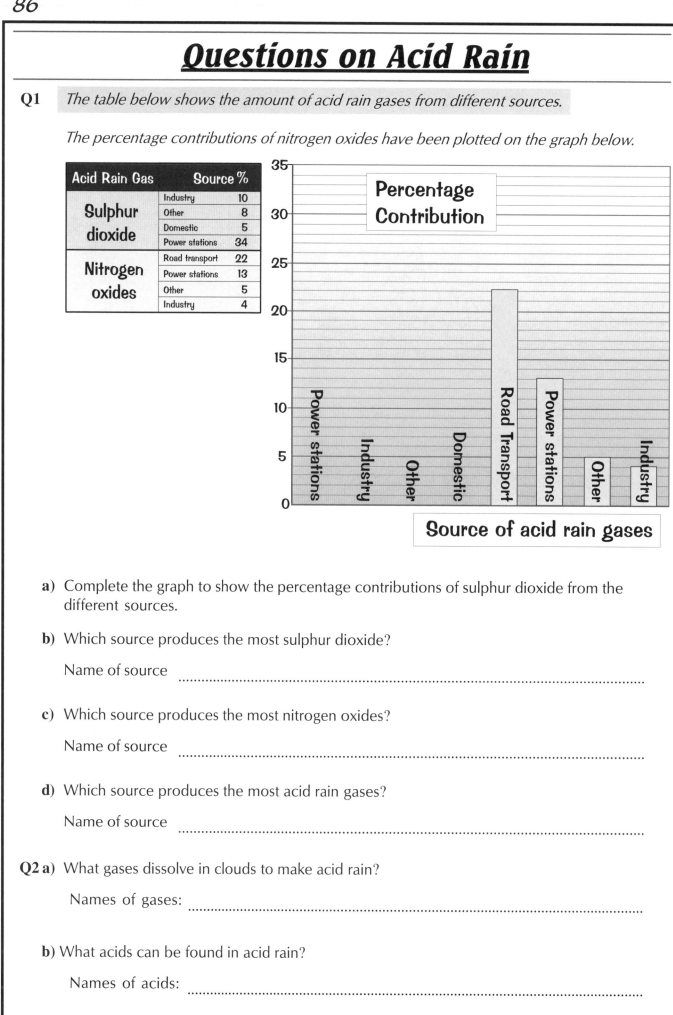

Acid Rain Gas	Source	%
Sulphur dioxide	Industry	10
	Other	8
	Domestic	5
	Power stations	34
Nitrogen oxides	Road transport	22
	Power stations	13
	Other	5
	Industry	4

a) Complete the graph to show the percentage contributions of sulphur dioxide from the different sources.

b) Which source produces the most sulphur dioxide?

Name of source ....

c) Which source produces the most nitrogen oxides?

Name of source ....

d) Which source produces the most acid rain gases?

Name of source ....

Q2 a) What gases dissolve in clouds to make acid rain?

Names of gases: ....

b) What acids can be found in acid rain?

Names of acids: ....

Questions on Farming and its Problems

Q1 Look at this food chain, then answer the questions:

| rose bush ⟹ greenfly ⟹ ladybird ⟹ great tit |

a) Circle the correct answer from each of the <u>underlined</u> pairs:

Insecticide will kill the <u>rose bush</u> / <u>greenfly</u>.

Ladybirds eat <u>great tits</u> / <u>greenfly</u>.

If there are fewer greenfly, there will be <u>more</u> / <u>less</u> food for the great tits.

b) Look at your answers to part a). Explain briefly what might happen to great tits if a gardener uses an insecticide spray to protect their rose bushes.

....

....

Q2 a) Put a tick in the box next to each correct sentence about *pesticides:*

Pesticides kill insects.	
If pesticides kill bees, more flowers will be pollinated.	
The use of pesticides provides more food for many birds.	

b) Look at the sentences without a tick. Write down the correct versions of the sentences.

....

....

Q3 *Complete the sentences below using the words from the list:*

fish fertilisers insects minerals pollinating chains pesticides oxygen
Farmers use .... to kill .... and other
pests that reduce crop yields. The use of these chemicals can disturb food
.... and reduce the number of .... insects.
Farmers use .... to replace lost .... in the
soil, but they can cause the amount of .... in rivers to
decrease, and so reduce the number of .... and other animals.

Section Six — The Environment

Questions on Pyramids of Numbers & Biomass

Q1   *Look at this food chain:* carrot → rabbit → fox

    a) What food does the rabbit eat? ....

    b) In the food chain, there were 4000 carrots, 100 rabbits, and 1 fox.
        Which pyramid of numbers below, **A**, **B** or **C**, is the correct one for this food chain?

        Correct pyramid is ....

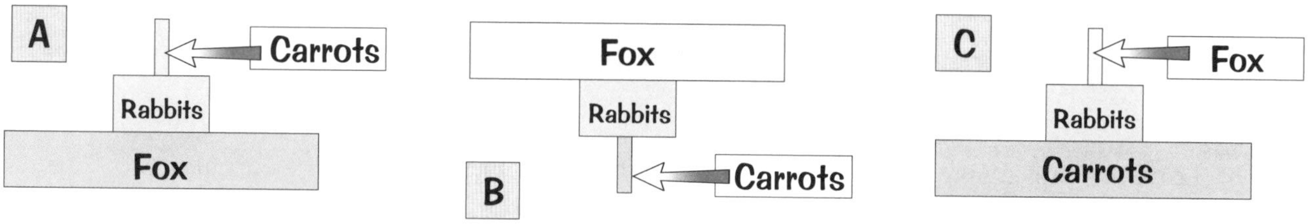

A
Carrots
Rabbits
Fox

Fox
Rabbits
Carrots
B

C
Fox
Rabbits
Carrots

Q2   *The diagram below is a pyramid of numbers. The bar showing the tertiary consumers has been labelled for you. The other bars have not.*

    Identify which bar corresponds to the other letters.

Bar	⟹	Letter
producers		A
secondary consumers		B
primary consumers		C

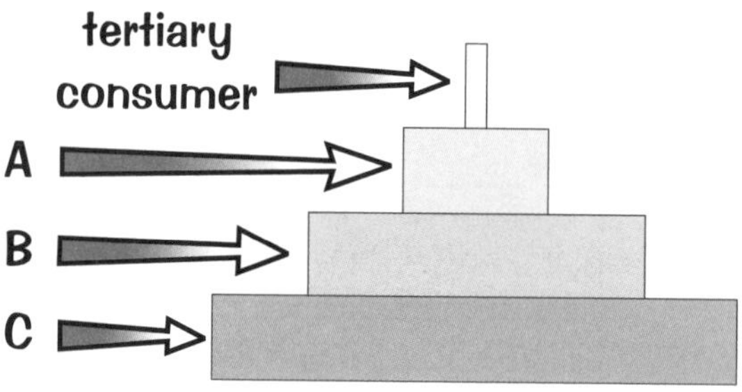

tertiary consumer ⟹

A ⟹
B ⟹
C ⟹

Q3   Draw pyramids of numbers for the following food chains. Use the space at the bottom of the page. When you draw your pyramids, make sure you do the following things:

    Use a ruler and sharp pencil.

    Label each step with the name and number of the living thing.

    a) tiny plants (10,000)   →   water fleas (2,000)   →   trout (1)

    b) rose bush (1)   →   greenfly (100)   →   ladybirds (20)   →   great tit (2)

Pyramid a)	Pyramid b)

Questions on Pyramids of Numbers & Biomass

Q4 *Read the following sentences about biomass and pyramids of biomass and put a tick in the boxes next to the correct sentences.*

Biomass is the number of living things. ☐

Biomass is the mass of living material. ☐

Pyramids of biomass show the biomass at each stage in a food chain. ☐

Pyramids of biomass cannot be drawn to scale. ☐

The biomass decreases from the beginning to the end of a food chain. ☐

Q5 *One of the food chains in the North Sea is:*

tiny plants → tiny animals → mackerel → cod.

The biomass of each living thing is shown in the table.

organism	biomass in kg
cod	2
mackerel	10
tiny animals	80
tiny plants	100

Draw the pyramid of biomass for this food chain in the space below. I suggest you use a scale of 1mm for each kg.

Questions on Pyramids of Numbers & Biomass

Q6   *Look at the pyramid on the right.*

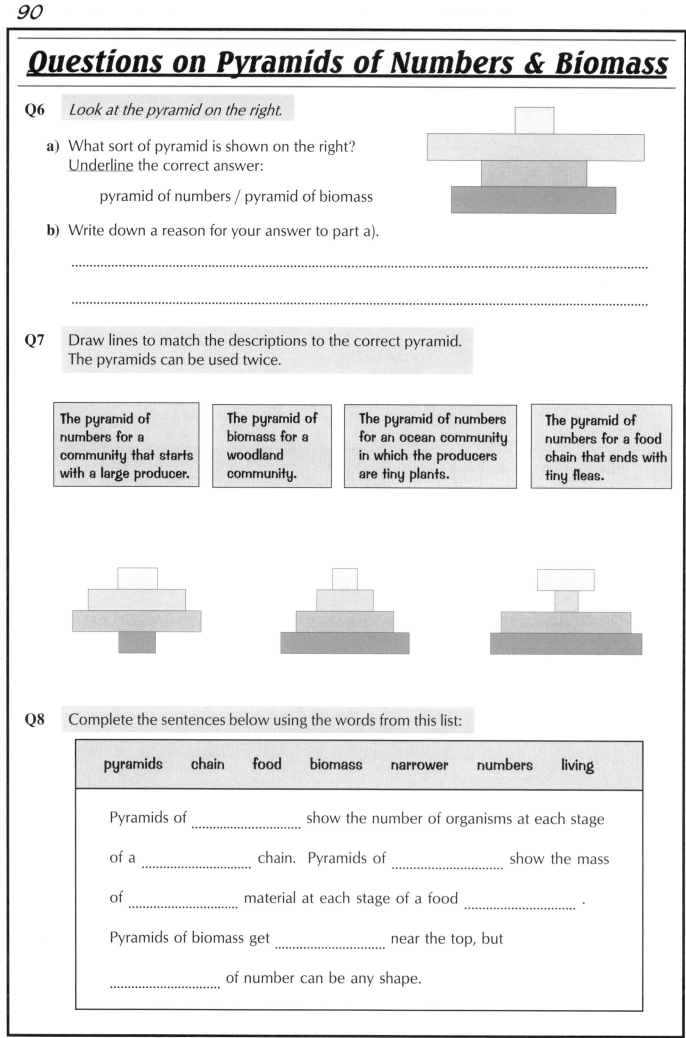

   a)   What sort of pyramid is shown on the right?
Underline the correct answer:

   pyramid of numbers / pyramid of biomass

   b)   Write down a reason for your answer to part a).

   ....

   ....

Q7   Draw lines to match the descriptions to the correct pyramid.
The pyramids can be used twice.

The pyramid of numbers for a community that starts with a large producer.	The pyramid of biomass for a woodland community.	The pyramid of numbers for an ocean community in which the producers are tiny plants.	The pyramid of numbers for a food chain that ends with tiny fleas.

Q8   Complete the sentences below using the words from this list:

pyramids   chain   food   biomass   narrower   numbers   living

Pyramids of .... show the number of organisms at each stage

of a .... chain. Pyramids of .... show the mass

of .... material at each stage of a food ....

Pyramids of biomass get .... near the top, but

.... of number can be any shape.

Questions on The Carbon Cycle

Q1 *There are two equations you need to know: one for photosynthesis and one for respiration.*

    a) Complete the word equation below for photosynthesis:

        Carbon dioxide   + ...   →   glucose   + ...

    b) Complete the word equation below for respiration:

        ....   +   oxygen   →   water   + ...

Q2 The diagram below shows part of the carbon cycle. Use your answers to question 1 to fill in the missing words. Choose from the list below left (you will not need them all):

photosynthesis respiration oxygen carbon dioxide water glucose	.... **in the atmosphere** .... **Carbon Compounds in plants**

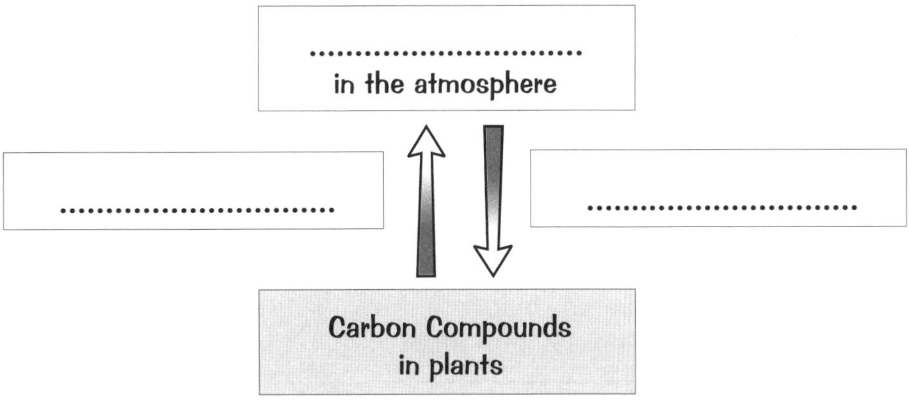

Q3 a) What gas, found in air, is needed for burning to happen? ....

    b) *Water vapour is produced when wood burns.*
    What other gas is produced when wood burns? ....

    c) Complete the word equation for wood burning. Use your answers to parts a) and b) to help you.

        wood   + ...   →   ....   + ...

Q4 Fill in the missing words in the sentences below. Choose from this list of words:

glucose   up   down   respiration   oxygen   photosynthesis   burn   carbon dioxide
Plants make glucose from .... and water. This process is called .... It causes the amount of carbon dioxide in the air to go .... Animals, plants and bacteria produce energy from .... using the process called .... This process causes the amount of carbon dioxide in the air to go .... When wood and other fuels .... , ... from the air is used up, and more carbon dioxide is produced.

Questions on The Carbon Cycle

Q5 *Bacteria and fungi are decomposers. They can break down solid waste materials from animals. They can also break down materials in dead animals and plants. This breakdown is called decay.*

a) What can decomposers do? ....

....

b) What is decay? ....

....

c) Name two types of living thing that can cause decay: .... and ....

Q6 Complete these sentences about decay by microbes.
Circle the correct word from each of the underlined pairs:

a) Microbes break down materials faster when they are cool /warm, and in moist / dry conditions.

b) Many microbes work better if there is more oxygen / nitrogen in their environment.

Q7 Match the statements below to show the effect the three processes have on the amount of carbon dioxide in the air.

| photosynthesis causes |
| decay (decomposition) causes |
| burning and respiration cause |

| carbon dioxide in the air to increase |
| carbon dioxide in the air to decrease |

Q8 *Look at the diagram of the carbon cycle below.*

Fill in the missing words to complete the diagram. Choose from the list below (some words may not be needed, and some words might be needed more than once):

| animals   plants   decay   burning   feeding   respiration   photosynthesis |

carbon dioxide in the atmosphere

....

Respiration, decay and ....

....

oil and natural gas

Respiration and ....

carbon compounds in ....

....

carbon compounds in ....

ANSWERS

These are for checking, NOT COPYING, be warned.

Biology

Foundation Level

Questions on Cells

Q1 Both the house and the human body are built up of smaller building blocks.

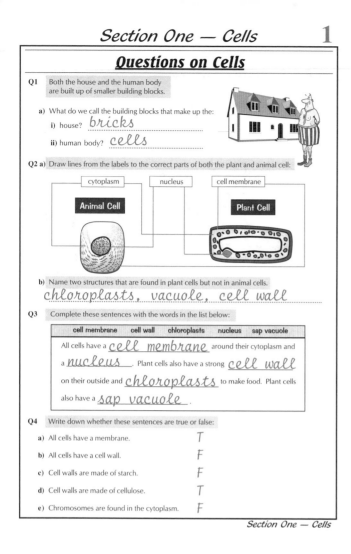

a) What do we call the building blocks that make up the:

i) house? *bricks*

ii) human body? *cells*

Q2 a) Draw lines from the labels to the correct parts of both the plant and animal cell:

cytoplasm   nucleus   cell membrane

Animal Cell   **Plant Cell**

b) Name two structures that are found in plant cells but not in animal cells.
chloroplasts, vacuole, cell wall

Q3 Complete these sentences with the words in the list below:

cell membrane	cell wall	chloroplasts	nucleus	sap vacuole

All cells have a *cell membrane* around their cytoplasm and a *nucleus*. Plant cells also have a strong *cell wall* on their outside and *chloroplasts* to make food. Plant cells also have a *sap vacuole*.

Q4 Write down whether these sentences are true or false:

a) All cells have a membrane. *T*

b) All cells have a cell wall. *F*

c) Cell walls are made of starch. *F*

d) Cell walls are made of cellulose. *T*

e) Chromosomes are found in the cytoplasm. *F*

Questions on Cells

Q5 This is a diagram of a human sperm cell.

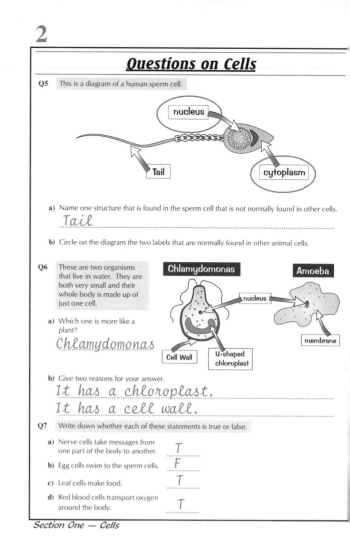

nucleus

Tail   cytoplasm

a) Name one structure that is found in the sperm cell that is not normally found in other cells.
Tail

b) Circle on the diagram the two labels that are normally found in other animal cells.

Q6 These are two organisms that live in water. They are both very small and their whole body is made up of just one cell.

Chlamydomonas   Amoeba

nucleus

Cell Wall   U-shaped chloroplast   membrane

a) Which one is more like a plant?
Chlamydomonas

b) Give two reasons for your answer.
It has a chloroplast.
It has a cell wall.

Q7 Write down whether each of these statements is true or false.

a) Nerve cells take messages from one part of the body to another. *T*

b) Egg cells swim to the sperm cells. *F*

c) Leaf cells make food. *T*

d) Red blood cells transport oxygen around the body. *T*

3

Questions on Specialised Cells

Q1 Eggs are cells. The ostrich egg is the largest cell in the world.

a) Name three parts of an egg that make it a cell. *Nucleus, cytoplasm (white), cell membrane*

b) What is the job of an egg cell?
Sexual reproduction

Q2 These are cells that do special jobs.

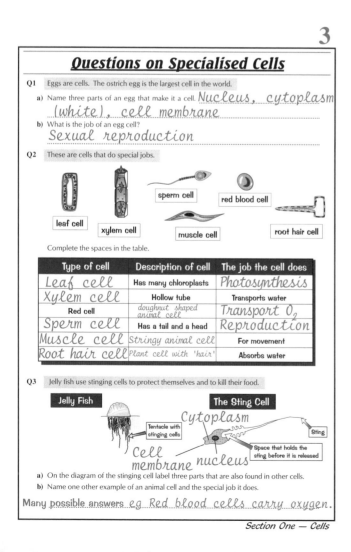

sperm cell   red blood cell

leaf cell   xylem cell   muscle cell   root hair cell

Complete the spaces in the table.

Type of cell	Description of cell	The job the cell does
Leaf cell	Has many chloroplasts	*Photosynthesis*
Xylem cell	Hollow tube	Transports water
Red cell	doughnut shaped animal cell	*Transport O$_2$*
Sperm cell	Has a tail and a head	*Reproduction*
Muscle cell	*Stringy animal cell*	For movement
Root hair cell	*Plant cell with 'hair'*	Absorbs water

Q3 Jelly fish use stinging cells to protect themselves and to kill their food.

Jelly Fish   The Sting Cell

Cytoplasm

Tentacle with stinging cells   Sting

Cell membrane *nucleus*   Space that holds the sting before it is released

a) On the diagram of the stinging cell label three parts that are also found in other cells.

b) Name one other example of an animal cell and the special job it does.
Many possible answers eg Red blood cells carry oxygen.

Questions on Diffusion

Q1 The diagram shows part of a leaf. Gases go in and out of leaves by diffusion.

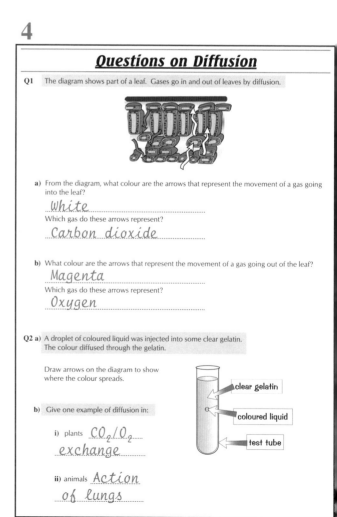

a) From the diagram, what colour are the arrows that represent the movement of a gas going into the leaf?
White
Which gas do these arrows represent?
Carbon dioxide

b) What colour are the arrows that represent the movement of a gas going out of the leaf?
Magenta
Which gas do these arrows represent?
Oxygen

Q2 a) A droplet of coloured liquid was injected into some clear gelatin. The colour diffused through the gelatin.

Draw arrows on the diagram to show where the colour spreads.

clear gelatin

coloured liquid

test tube

b) Give one example of diffusion in:

i) plants *CO$_2$/O$_2$ exchange*

ii) animals *Action of lungs*

Questions on Diffusion

Q3 Gases diffuse (spread) from a high concentration (many particles) to a low concentration (few particles). This occurs in the air sacs in a lung (diagram opposite).

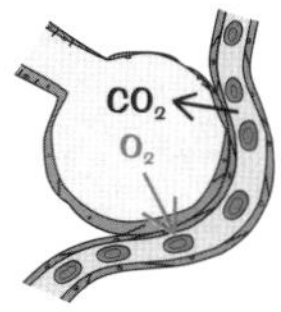

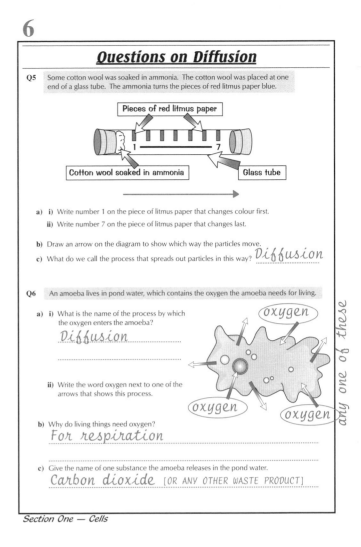

CO₂
O₂

a) Draw arrow heads on the lines to show which way the oxygen and carbon dioxide particles move.

b) Complete the table by ticking the correct boxes.

Part of Lung	Concentration of oxygen		Concentration of carbon dioxide	
	Low (few particles)	High (many particles)	Low (few particles)	High (many particles)
Blood vessel going to lung	✓			✓
Air sac		✓	✓	

Q4 Diffusion is a very important process in living things. Many parts of living things have become adapted to make diffusion happen more quickly.

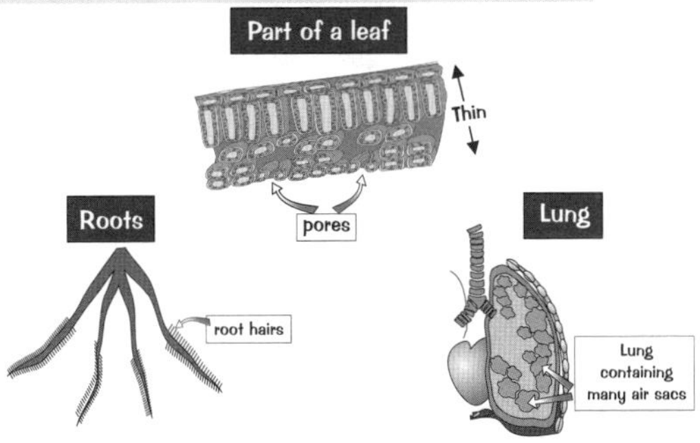

Part of a leaf

Thin

Roots
pores
Lung

root hairs

Lung containing many air sacs

Use the information in the diagrams to give one adaptation in each of these structures.

a) Roots *Hairs increase surface area for diffusion.*

b) Leaves *Thinness makes distances small OR spaces allow movement of gas.*

c) Lungs *Air sacs give a very large surface area.*

6

Questions on Diffusion

Q5 Some cotton wool was soaked in ammonia. The cotton wool was placed at one end of a glass tube. The ammonia turns the pieces of red litmus paper blue.

Pieces of red litmus paper

1   7

Cotton wool soaked in ammonia   Glass tube

a) **i)** Write number 1 on the piece of litmus paper that changes colour first.

ii) Write number 7 on the piece of litmus paper that changes last.

b) Draw an arrow on the diagram to show which way the particles move.

c) What do we call the process that spreads out particles in this way? *Diffusion*

Q6 An amoeba lives in pond water, which contains the oxygen the amoeba needs for living.

a) **i)** What is the name of the process by which the oxygen enters the amoeba?

Diffusion

oxygen

ii) Write the word oxygen next to one of the arrows that shows this process.

oxygen   oxygen

any one of these

b) Why do living things need oxygen? *For respiration*

c) Give the name of one substance the amoeba releases in the pond water. *Carbon dioxide* [OR ANY OTHER WASTE PRODUCT]

SECTION TWO — PLANTS

7

Questions on Plant Structure

Q1 A plant is made up of three parts.

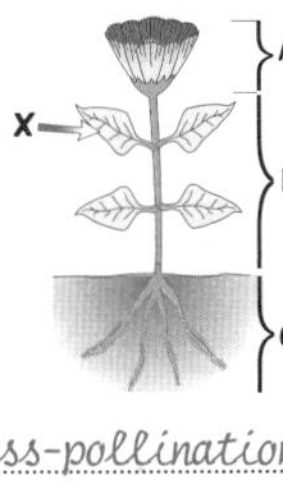

A *Flower*

X

B *Stem*

C *Root*

a) Label parts A, B and C.

b) What do we call X? *Leaf*

c) Explain in one sentence what each part of the plant does.

A *Attracts insects for cross-pollination/reproduction*

B *Supports plant/takes it towards light*

C *Collects water & minerals from soil OR support*

Q2 Draw lines to connect the part of the plant with the correct function it does.

Plant part	→	Function
stems		absorb water
roots		carry leaves
leaves		make food
flowers		seeds are made here

Q3 Use the words to fill in the spaces.

flower   leaves   minerals   petals   roots   reproductive   seeds   stem   water

Plants are made up of three parts, the _flower_ , the stem and the _roots_ which are found under the ground. The roots hold the plant firmly in the ground. They also absorb _water_ with dissolved _minerals_ from the soil. The _stem_ has the job of holding the plant upright. This helps the leaves to catch more light. The _leaves_ are responsible for making food. The flowers contain the _reproductive_ parts of the plant. These are found inside the _petals_ . When the flower dies, _seeds_ are released.

8

Questions on Plant Structure

Q4 The diagram shows the parts of a cabbage plant that are eaten by pest animals.

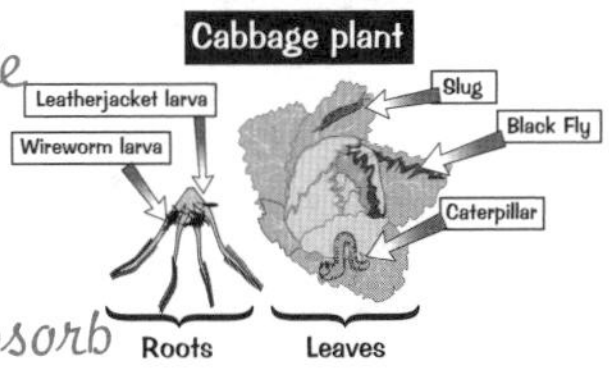

a) More pest animals feed off the leaves than the roots. Why do you think this is?

Leaves are accessible and often contain more food.

Cabbage plant

Leatherjacket larva   Slug
Wireworm larva   Black Fly
          Caterpillar
Roots   Leaves

b) Why does the plant die when its roots are eaten?

It can no longer absorb enough water/minerals.

c) Where would we find the animals that eat the roots of plants?

In the soil OR on/in the roots

Q5 The Colorado beetle has spread from Colorado in America to much of Europe. It has been found in the UK since 1901. Both the beetles and their larvae (caterpillar like animals) feed on the leaves of potato plants.

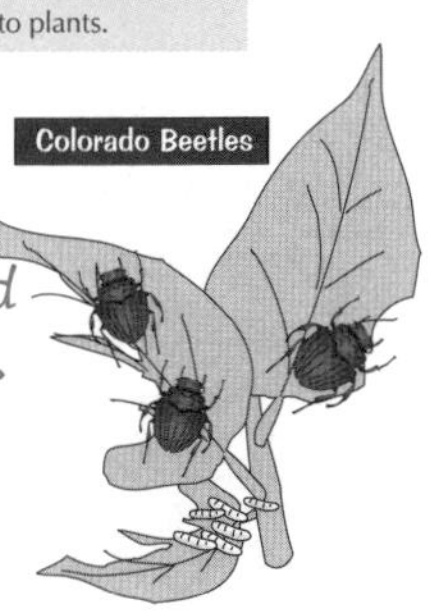

a) Why are leaves important to a plant?

They make food for the plant by Photosynthesis [which provides material and energy for growth and life].

Colorado Beetles

b) What happens to a plant if its leaves are eaten?

It dies if all are eaten.

c) Name one other garden animal that eats leaves.

Caterpillars OR other sensible answer

Questions on Leaf Structure

Q1 The diagram opposite shows part of a leaf.

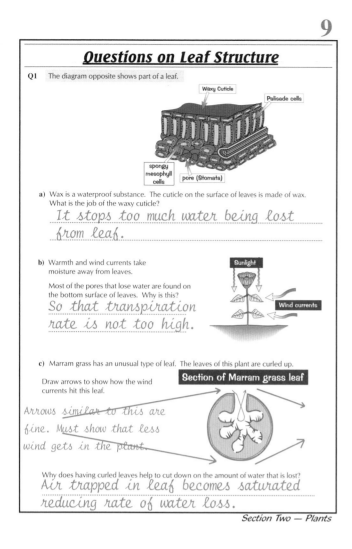

a) Wax is a waterproof substance. The cuticle on the surface of leaves is made of wax. What is the job of the waxy cuticle?

It stops too much water being lost from leaf.

b) Warmth and wind currents take moisture away from leaves.

Most of the pores that lose water are found on the bottom surface of leaves. Why is this?

So that transpiration rate is not too high.

c) Marram grass has an unusual type of leaf. The leaves of this plant are curled up.

Draw arrows to show how the wind currents hit this leaf.

Arrows similar to this are fine. Must show that less wind gets in the plant.

Why does having curled leaves help to cut down on the amount of water that is lost?

Air trapped in leaf becomes saturated reducing rate of water loss.

Section Two — Plants

Questions on Leaf Structure

Q2 Plants whose leaves float on water have more pores on the top surface of their leaves.

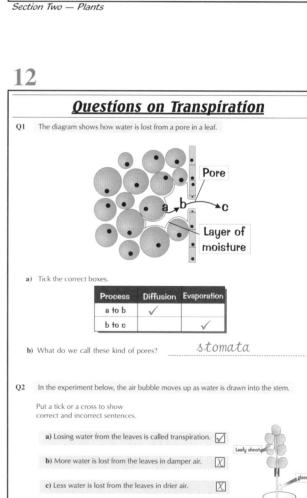

Why do you think this is?

Pores must open to the air for transpiration to work.

Q3 Leaves are darker on their top surface. This is because they have more of the green substance, called chlorophyll, in the cells near the top surface.

a) Light from the sun hits the leaves. Draw on the diagram opposite an arrow showing the direction the light is coming from.

b) Why is it better to have more of the green substance (Chlorophyll) in the top surface of the leaf?

The chlorophyll gets more light so photosynthesis is more productive.

Q4 Match the description on the left with the correct part of the leaf.

description → part

green substance is called — chlorophyll
they contain chlorophyll — chloroplasts
cells that contain the green substance — leaf cells

Section Two — Plants

Questions on Leaf Structure

Q5 Some plants have green and white areas. This is called variegated leaves.

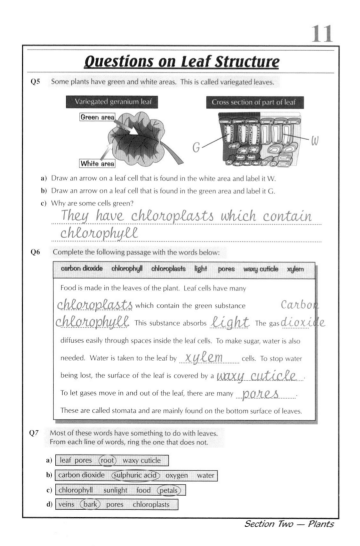

a) Draw an arrow on a leaf cell that is found in the white area and label it W.
b) Draw an arrow on a leaf cell that is found in the green area and label it G.
c) Why are some cells green?

They have chloroplasts which contain chlorophyll

Q6 Complete the following passage with the words below:

carbon dioxide   chlorophyll   chloroplasts   light   pores   waxy cuticle   xylem

Food is made in the leaves of the plant. Leaf cells have many *chloroplasts* which contain the green substance *carbon chlorophyll* This substance absorbs *light* The gas *dioxide* diffuses easily through spaces inside the leaf cells. To make sugar, water is also needed. Water is taken to the leaf by *xylem* cells. To stop water being lost, the surface of the leaf is covered by a *waxy cuticle* To let gases move in and out of the leaf, there are many *pores*. These are called stomata and are mainly found on the bottom surface of leaves.

Q7 Most of these words have something to do with leaves. From each line of words, ring the one that does not.

a) leaf pores (root) waxy cuticle
b) carbon dioxide (sulphuric acid) oxygen water
c) chlorophyll sunlight food (petals)
d) veins (bark) pores chloroplasts

Section Two — Plants

Questions on Transpiration

Q1 The diagram shows how water is lost from a pore in a leaf.

a) Tick the correct boxes.

Process	Diffusion	Evaporation
a to b	✓	
b to c		✓

b) What do we call these kind of pores? *stomata*

Q2 In the experiment below, the air bubble moves up as water is drawn into the stem.

Put a tick or a cross to show correct and incorrect sentences.

a) Losing water from the leaves is called transpiration. ✓
b) More water is lost from the leaves in damper air. ✗
c) Less water is lost from the leaves in drier air. ✗
d) More water is lost in windy conditions. ✓
e) The name of a pore in the leaves is xylem. ✗

Section Two — Plants

13

Questions on Transpiration

Q3 This experiment shows water being lost from a clay pot. Clay pots have a large number of tiny holes.

a) How is the pot similar to a leaf?

It loses water by evaporation.

b) Give one way that the pot is different from the leaf.

It does not photosynthesise. OR any other sensible answer

c) Say how each of these conditions affects the amount of water lost from the pot.

i) very damp air _Reduces it_

ii) very hot air _Increases it_

iii) air that is not moving _Reduces it_

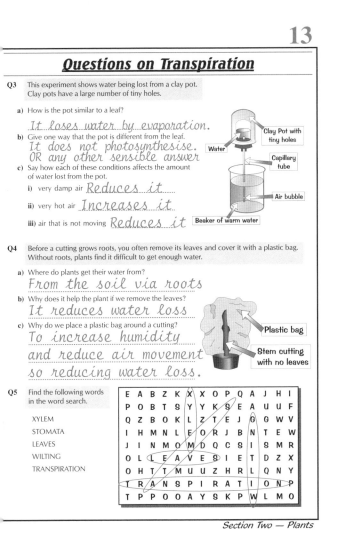

Q4 Before a cutting grows roots, you often remove its leaves and cover it with a plastic bag. Without roots, plants find it difficult to get enough water.

a) Where do plants get their water from?

From the soil via roots

b) Why does it help the plant if we remove the leaves?

It reduces water loss

c) Why do we place a plastic bag around a cutting?

To increase humidity and reduce air movement so reducing water loss.

Q5 Find the following words in the word search.

XYLEM
STOMATA
LEAVES
WILTING
TRANSPIRATION

E	A	B	Z	K	X	X	O	P	Q	A	J	H	I
P	O	B	T	S	Y	Y	K	S	E	A	U	U	F
Q	Z	B	O	K	L	Z	T	E	J	G	G	W	V
I	H	M	N	L	F	O	R	J	B	N	T	E	W
J	I	N	M	O	M	D	Q	C	S	I	S	M	R
O	L	E	A	V	E	S	I	E	T	D	Z	X	
O	H	T	T	M	U	U	Z	H	R	L	Q	N	Y
T	R	A	N	S	P	I	R	A	T	I	O	N	P
T	P	P	O	O	A	Y	S	K	P	W	L	M	O

Section Two — Plants

14

Questions on Transport Systems in Plants

Q1 Plants get their water from the soil. This water is later lost to the atmosphere.

a) Use these words to complete the flow diagram.

leaves	roots	stem

SOIL ⟹ _roots_ ⟹ _stem_ ⟹ _leaves_ ⟹ ATMOSPHERE

b) i) What cells transport water? _xylem_

ii) What else do these cells carry? _minerals_

c) What cells carry sugar (dissolved food)? _phloem_

Q2 The diagram shows the path water takes through a plant.

a) What carries water from **d** to **f**?

xylem cells

b) To get to **g**, water escapes from little holes in the leaves.

i) What are these holes called?

stomata

ii) What do we call this process?

transpiration

c) Food is made in the leaves and stored in the roots.

i) What cells carry the food?

phloem

ii) Draw arrows to show the journey of the food.

iii) Colour the arrows showing the journey of food in red and the journey of water in blue.

iv) Add a key of all the arrows to the diagram.

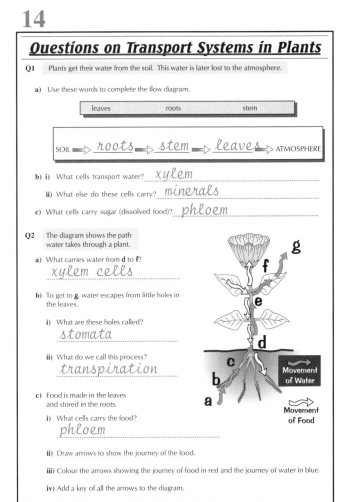

Section Two — Plants

15

Questions on Transport Systems in Plants

Q3 This is a diagram of a plum tree. The plums are full of sugar which is made in the leaves of the tree.

a) How does the sugar get from the leaves to the plums?

It is carried dissolved in water in the phloem cells.

The reason fruits like plums are swollen is because they are also full of water.

b) i) Where did the water originally come from?

The soil

ii) How does the water get to the plum fruits?

Via the root and xylem cells

Q4 Opposite is a section of a stem, showing the xylem and phloem cells.

a) What is the job of the xylem cells?

To transport water

b) What is the job of the phloem cells?

To transport food

c) Why do the ends of the xylem and phloem cells have a large opening?

To allow fluid to flow from one cell to next

d) Why are xylem and phloem cells hollow?

So substance can flow through them.

e) Why are xylem and phloem cells sometimes called the 'plumbing' of the plant?

They are living pipes / carry water around the plant.

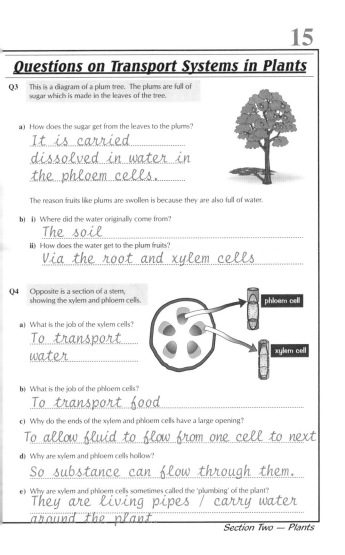

16

Questions on Photosynthesis

Q1 The diagram shows what the leaves need to make food.

a) Use the words in the box below to fill in the blanks on the diagram.

chlorophyll	air
oxygen	air
carbon dioxide	
sunlight	water

Oxygen is released into the _air_

sunlight for energy is absorbed by _chlorophyll_

Carbon dioxide from the _air_

water from the soil

b) Name the process involved in making food.

Photosynthesis

c) What is the name of the food produced?

sugar, glucose, starch

Q2 Complete the table, to show the differences between photosynthesis and respiration.

	Photosynthesis	Respiration
Raw materials used	CO_2, H_2O	O_2, glucose
End products	Glucose, O_2	CO_2, H_2O
Purpose of process	Store light's energy	Release stored energy

Q3 Adam set up a bottle garden. Inside the bottle he grew some plants and placed a butterfly he'd caught in his garden. He knew the butterfly fed on sugar, so he placed a dish of sugary water inside the bottle. Just before going on a two week holiday to Corfu, Adam caught another butterfly. He placed this butterfly in another bottle, but he did not have time to add the plants. The diagrams show what he saw when he returned from holiday.

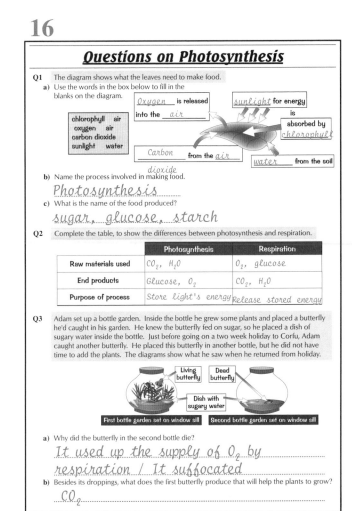

a) Why did the butterfly in the second bottle die?

It used up the supply of O_2 by respiration / It suffocated

b) Besides its droppings, what does the first butterfly produce that will help the plants to grow?

_CO_2_

Section Two — Plants

Questions on Nutrition

Q1 Complete the sentences below about three nutrients. Choose the correct words from this list.

| cell membranes | growth | energy | proteins | fats |

Carbohydrates are needed to provide *energy* for the body.

proteins are needed for *growth* and repair.

Energy is supplied by *fats*, which are also needed to make *cell membranes*.

Q2 *You should be able to remember foods that are good sources of the three main nutrients.*

a) Write down two examples of foods that are good sources of *carbohydrate*.

Food 1 *Pasta, bread* Food 2 *Potatoes, cereals*

b) Write down two examples of foods that are good sources of *protein*.

Food 1 *Meat, eggs* Food 2 *Fish, pulses*

c) Write down two examples of foods that are good sources of *fat*.

Food 1 *Meat (some)* Food 2 *Butter, oil*

Q3 *We need 20–30g of dietary fibre (roughage) a day.*
A can of baked beans contains over 20g of dietary fibre.

a) Put a tick ✓ in the box ☐ next to each correct sentence about dietary fibre:

☐ Dietary fibre is needed to provide our bodies with carbohydrates for energy.

☑ Dietary fibre helps to prevent constipation if we eat enough of it.

☑ Raw fruit and vegetables are good sources of dietary fibre.

b) One sentence is incorrect. Write down a correct version of it in the space below.

Dietry Fibre doesn't provide our bodies with carbohydrates

Q4 *It is often recommended that we drink plenty of water, and some foods also contain water.*

Why is water so important in our diet?

We need it to do everything / We lose a great deal every day.

Or any sensible answers

18

Questions on Food Tests

Q1 Match the four substances to the correct test which identifies the substance.

| substance | ⟹ | indicator test |

fat can be detected using — the emulsion test

protein can be detected using — the Biuret test

starch can be detected using — iodine solution

sugars can be detected using — Benedict's reagent

Q2 Iodine solution is used in food tests. What colour would you see when it is added to:

a) Sugar? *brown*

b) Starch? *blue/black*

c) Protein? *brown*

Q3 In the table below, complete the starting colour and end result for a *positive test* using Benedict's reagent.

colour at start *blue*

⬇

end result *orange precipitate*

Q4 Complete the instructions for the biuret test below. Choose from this list of words:

| purple | shake | sodium hydroxide | protein | copper sulphate |

The biuret test can be used to detect protein in food. You put some food in a test tube, and add some *sodium hydroxide*. You then give it a *shake*, and add some *copper sulphate* (this is blue). If it goes a *purple* colour, it means that *protein* is present.

19

Questions on The Digestive System

Q1 Use the information below to name these parts of the digestive system. One has been done for you.

Name	Appearance
large intestine	Broad rippled tube
gullet	Long tube leading from the mouth to the stomach
pancreas	Gland with rippled edges
small intestine	Coiled narrow tube, 3-5cm in diameter, about 6-7m long
stomach	Large container for food - holds about 1 litre

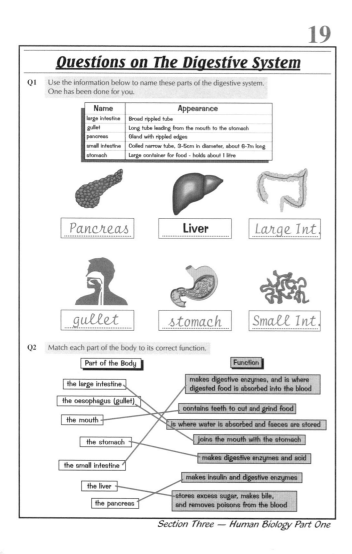

Pancreas **Liver** *Large Int.*

gullet *stomach* *Small Int.*

Q2 Match each part of the body to its correct function.

| Part of the Body | Function |

the large intestine — makes digestive enzymes, and is where digested food is absorbed into the blood

the oesophagus (gullet) — contains teeth to cut and grind food

the mouth — is where water is absorbed and faeces are stored

the stomach — joins the mouth with the stomach

the small intestine — makes digestive enzymes and acid

the liver — makes insulin and digestive enzymes

the pancreas — stores excess sugar, makes bile, and removes poisons from the blood

---

Questions on The Digestive System

Q3 Write the names of each part of the digestive system in the correct boxes below. Choose from the words in the box at the bottom of the page. One of them, the gall bladder, has been done for you.

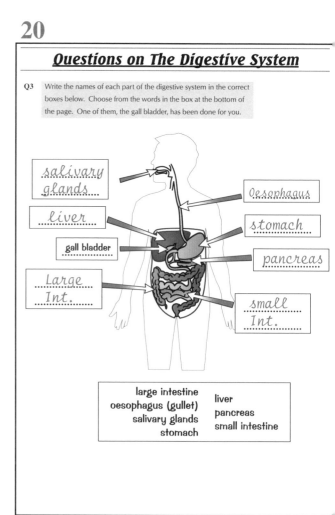

salivary glands

liver

gall bladder

Large Int.

Oesophagus

stomach

pancreas

small Int.

large intestine	liver
oesophagus (gullet)	pancreas
salivary glands	small intestine
stomach	

21

Questions on The Digestive System

Q4 Complete this crossword using the clues given below.

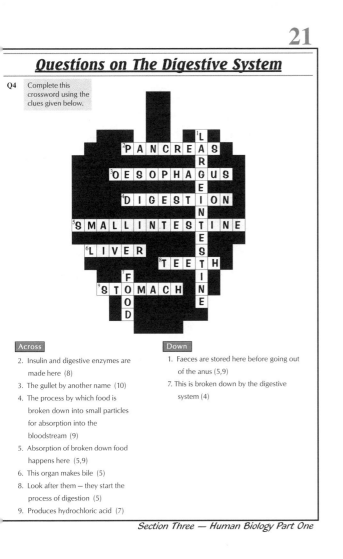

Across

2. Insulin and digestive enzymes are made here (8)
3. The gullet by another name (10)
4. The process by which food is broken down into small particles for absorption into the bloodstream (9)
5. Absorption of broken down food happens here (5,9)
6. This organ makes bile (5)
8. Look after them — they start the process of digestion (5)
9. Produces hydrochloric acid (7)

Down

1. Faeces are stored here before going out of the anus (5,9)
7. This is broken down by the digestive system (4)

Section Three — Human Biology Part One

22

Questions on Digestive Enzymes

Q1 Circle the correct words from each underlined pair in the following sentences:

a) A catalyst is a substance that is produced by / (speeds up) chemical reactions.

b) A catalyst is used up / (not used up) during the reaction. It can be used only once / (more than once.)

c) Different reactions need the same catalyst / (different catalysts.) Enzymes are artificial / (biological) catalysts. Enzymes are (proteins) / metals.

Q2 a) Put a tick in the box next to each correct sentence about digestion:

☑ In digestion, large molecules are broken down into small molecules.

☐ Digestive enzymes slow down digestion.

☑ The digestive system provides the right conditions for digestive enzymes to work well.

b) One sentence is incorrect. Write down a correct version of it in the space below.

Digestive enzymes speed up digestion.

Q3 *Gastric juice is added to food when it reaches the stomach. This juice contains an acid.*

a) Name the acid secreted by the stomach.

Hydrochloric

b) Estimate the pH of the stomach contents and give a reason for your answer.

2 to 6 - this is an acidic pH

c) Give two reasons why the stomach secretes this acid

It acts as a defence against invading microbes and supports the action of protease.

Section Three — Human Biology Part One

23

Questions on Digestive Enzymes

Q4 *You need to know about three types of digestive enzymes.*
Match the digestive enzymes to the substance that they break down:

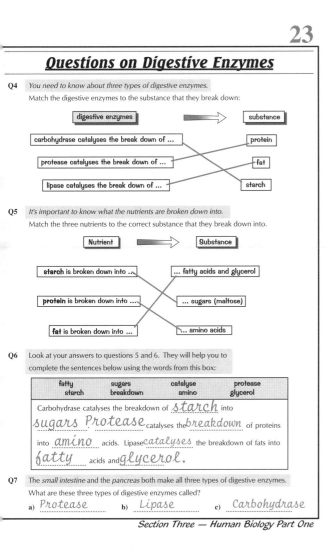

digestive enzymes → substance

carbohydrase catalyses the break down of ... → protein
protease catalyses the break down of ... → fat
lipase catalyses the break down of ... → starch

Q5 *It's important to know what the nutrients are broken down into.*
Match the three nutrients to the correct substance that they break down into.

Nutrient → Substance

starch is broken down into ... → ... fatty acids and glycerol
protein is broken down into ... → ... sugars (maltose)
fat is broken down into ... → ... amino acids

Q6 Look at your answers to questions 5 and 6. They will help you to complete the sentences below using the words from this box:

| fatty | sugars | catalyse | protease |
| starch | breakdown | amino | glycerol |

Carbohydrase catalyses the breakdown of *starch* into *sugars* Protease catalyses the *breakdown* of proteins into *amino* acids. Lipase *catalyses* the breakdown of fats into *fatty* acids and *glycerol.*

Q7 The *small intestine* and the *pancreas* both make all three types of digestive enzymes.
What are these three types of digestive enzymes called?

a) *Protease*   b) *Lipase*   c) *Carbohydrase*

Section Three — Human Biology Part One

Questions on Digestive Enzymes

Q9 The diagram below is a flow chart for the digestive system.

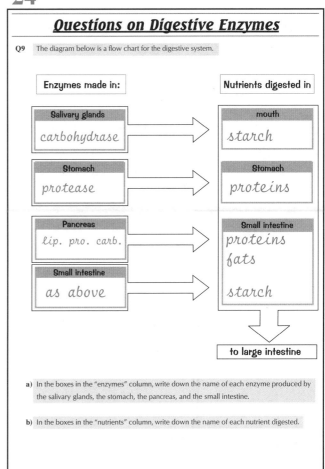

Enzymes made in:

Salivary glands — *carbohydrase*
Stomach — *protease*
Pancreas — *lip. pro. carb.*
Small intestine — *as above*

Nutrients digested in

mouth — *starch*
Stomach — *proteins*
Small intestine — *proteins fats starch*

to large intestine

a) In the boxes in the "enzymes" column, write down the name of each enzyme produced by the salivary glands, the stomach, the pancreas, and the small intestine.

b) In the boxes in the "nutrients" column, write down the name of each nutrient digested.

Section Three — Human Biology Part One

25

Questions on Absorption of Food

Q1 Angela was given a mixture of sand and sugar in a beaker.
She was asked to separate the sand from the sugar. Angela decided
to use the methods shown in the diagrams below to do this.

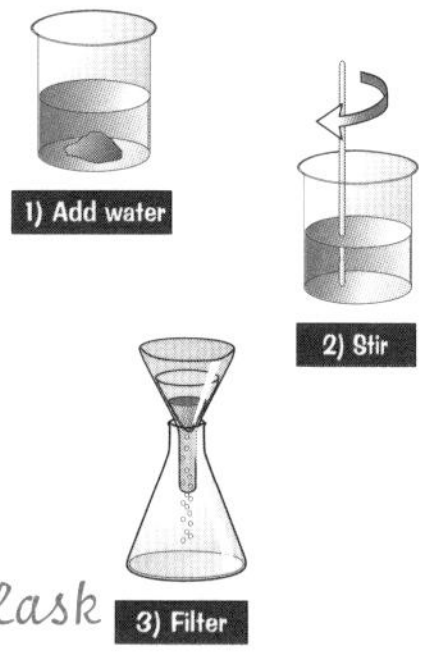

a) In steps 1 and 2, what happens to the sand?

It does not dissolve.

b) At the end of step 3, where will Angela find the sand?

In the filter paper

c) In steps 1 and 2, what happens to the sugar?

It dissolves

d) At the end of step 3, where will Angela find the sugar?

In the filtrate / in the flask

1) Add water

2) Stir

3) Filter

e) The pores in filter paper are so tiny that for particles to pass throught it they must be
dissolved in water. Why can sand be separated from sugar using Angela's method?

Its crystals are larger than the pores in the paper as it is not dissolved in the water.

Q2 Put these substances into the correct columns in the table.
Some substances are already in the table for you.

| amino acids | starch | fat | sugar | fatty acids |

soluble (dissolve in water)	insoluble (do not dissolve in water)
some proteins	some proteins
glycerol	*fat*
sugar	*starch*
fatty acids	
amino acids	

Section Three — Human Biology Part One

26

Questions on Absorption of Food

Q3 The digestive system breaks down food into small molecules that dissolve in water.
For revision, match the food being digested to the correct substance that is created.

| Food being digested | ⟹ | Substance |

- starch is digested to form... → amino acids
- protein is digested to form... → sugar
- fat is digested to form... → fatty acids and glycerol

Q4 Solve the absorption crossword.

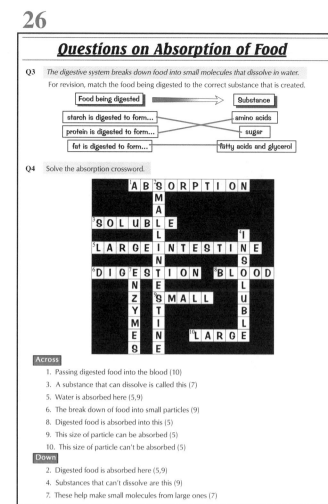

Across

1. Passing digested food into the blood (10)
3. A substance that can dissolve is called this (7)
5. Water is absorbed here (5,9)
6. The break down of food into small particles (9)
8. Digested food is absorbed into this (5)
9. This size of particle can be absorbed (5)
10. This size of particle can't be absorbed (5)

Down

2. Digested food is absorbed here (5,9)
4. Substances that can't dissolve are this (9)
7. These help make small molecules from large ones (7)

Section Three — Human Biology Part One

27

Questions on The Circulatory System

Q1 There are two main components of the circulatory system. One organ has a circuit all to
itself and its artery carries deoxygenated blood. Which organ is this?

Lungs

Q2 a) Put a tick in the box next to each correct sentence about the circulatory system:

☐ The circulatory system transports oxygen from the cells to the lungs.

☑ The circulatory system distributes heat and hormones around the body.

☑ The circulatory system transports wastes away from the cells in the body.

b) Write down a correct version of the incorrect sentence in the space below.

Circ syst. transp. Oxygen from the lungs to the cells

Q3 The diagram below shows the main features of the circulatory system. Deoxygenated
blood is represented by grey lines, and oxygenated blood by black lines. The arrows show
the direction of movement of the blood.

Use your knowledge and the clues in the diagram to match the labels 1 — 3 with the
following blood vessels:

| **Blood vessels:** | Pulmonary vein | Aorta | Vena cava |

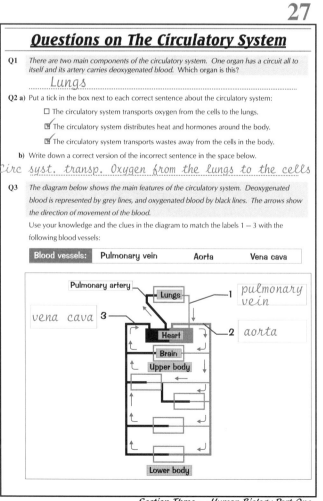

1 — *pulmonary vein*

3 — *vena cava*

2 — *aorta*

Section Three — Human Biology Part One

28

Questions on The Circulatory System

Q4 From the evidence in the diagram and your answers in Question 3, what is the difference
between an *artery* and a *vein*? Put a tick in the box next to the correct sentence:

☑ Arteries carry oxygenated blood and veins carry deoxygenated blood.

☐ Veins carry oxygenated blood and arteries carry deoxygenated blood.

☑ Arteries carry blood from the heart and veins carry blood to the heart.

☐ Veins carry blood from the heart and arteries carry blood to the heart.

Q5 What is the function of the heart in the circulatory system?

It's a pump / pushes the blood round

Q6 Why is this system called the circulatory system?

Because blood goes around and around

Q7 The diagram on the right shows the
human heart drawn as a simple
engineering drawing, rather than as a
cross-section of a real heart.

— The arrows show the
movement of blood.

— The valves are shown in grey.

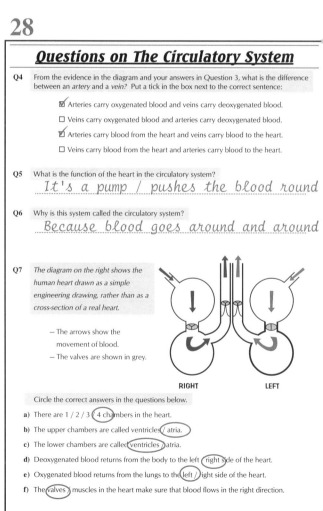

RIGHT   LEFT

Circle the correct answers in the questions below.

a) There are 1 / 2 / 3 / ④ chambers in the heart.

b) The upper chambers are called ventricles / ⟨atria⟩.

c) The lower chambers are called ⟨ventricles⟩ / atria.

d) Deoxygenated blood returns from the body to the left / ⟨right⟩ side of the heart.

e) Oxygenated blood returns from the lungs to the ⟨left⟩ / right side of the heart.

f) The ⟨valves⟩ / muscles in the heart make sure that blood flows in the right direction.

Section Three — Human Biology Part One

29

Questions on The Heart

Q1 You may be asked to label the parts of the heart. The diagram below shows a cross-section of the human heart drawn from the front. Match the labels to the correct names:

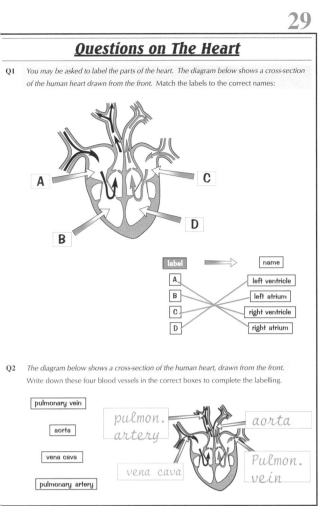

label		name
A		left ventricle
B		left atrium
C		right ventricle
D		right atrium

Q2 The diagram below shows a cross-section of the human heart, drawn from the front. Write down these four blood vessels in the correct boxes to complete the labelling.

pulmonary vein

aorta

vena cava

pulmonary artery

pulmon. artery   *aorta*   *vena cava*   *Pulmon. vein*

Section Three — Human Biology Part One

30

Questions on The Heart

Q3 Complete these sentences about the heart. Choose from the list of words below.

valves	muscle	body	blood	pumps	wall

The *wall* of the heart is mainly *muscle*. The heart *pumps* blood around the *body*. The *valves* prevent backflow of *blood*.

Q4 The diagram on the right shows the way the heart fits into the circulatory system. The left side pumps blood around the body.

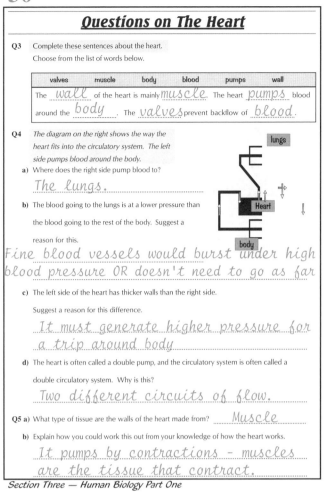

a) Where does the right side pump blood to?

The lungs.

b) The blood going to the lungs is at a lower pressure than the blood going to the rest of the body. Suggest a reason for this.

Fine blood vessels would burst under high blood pressure OR doesn't need to go as far

c) The left side of the heart has thicker walls than the right side. Suggest a reason for this difference.

It must generate higher pressure for a trip around body

d) The heart is often called a double pump, and the circulatory system is often called a double circulatory system. Why is this?

Two different circuits of flow.

Q5 a) What type of tissue are the walls of the heart made from? *Muscle*

b) Explain how you could work this out from your knowledge of how the heart works.

It pumps by contractions - muscles are the tissue that contract.

Section Three — Human Biology Part One

31

Questions on The Heart

Q6 The sentences below describe the steps needed for the heart to pump blood. Put a ring around the correct options of underlined words.

Blood enters the heart via [the left / the right] [either] [atrium / ventricle].
Blood leaves the heart when either [atrium / ventricle] [contracts / relaxes].
Valves make sure that the [blood / air] flows in the correct direction.
Contractions of the right atrium force blood into the [left / right] [artery / ventricle].
The pulmonary vein is odd in that it carries [oxygenated / deoxygenated] blood

Q7 Complete the crossword. The word answers are all to do with the heart.

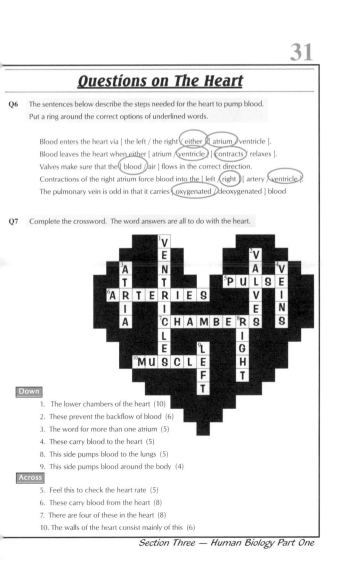

Down

1. The lower chambers of the heart (10)
2. These prevent the backflow of blood (6)
3. The word for more than one atrium (5)
4. These carry blood to the heart (5)
8. This side pumps blood to the lungs (5)
9. This side pumps blood around the body (4)

Across

5. Feel this to check the heart rate (5)
6. These carry blood from the heart (8)
7. There are four of these in the heart (8)
10. The walls of the heart consist mainly of this (6)

Section Three — Human Biology Part One

Questions on Blood Vessels

Q1 Circle the correct words in the underlined pairs in these two sentences about blood vessels.

Arteries carry blood to / from the heart at low / high pressure.
Veins carry blood to / from the heart at low / high pressure.

Q2 The diagrams on the right show cross-sections of blood vessels. They are not drawn to scale.

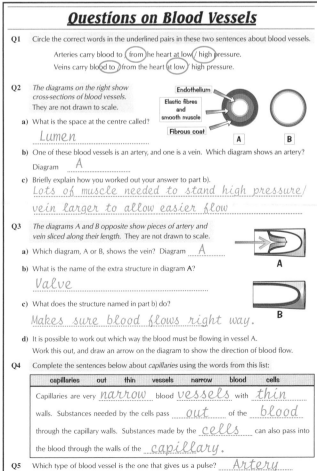

a) What is the space at the centre called?

Lumen

b) One of these blood vessels is an artery, and one is a vein. Which diagram shows an artery? Diagram *A*

c) Briefly explain how you worked out your answer to part b).

Lots of muscle needed to stand high pressure / vein larger to allow easier flow

Q3 The diagrams A and B opposite show pieces of artery and vein sliced along their length. They are not drawn to scale.

a) Which diagram, A or B, shows the vein? Diagram *A*

b) What is the name of the extra structure in diagram A?

Valve

c) What does the structure named in part b) do?

Makes sure blood flows right way.

d) It is possible to work out which way the blood must be flowing in vessel A. Work this out, and draw an arrow on the diagram to show the direction of blood flow.

Q4 Complete the sentences below about *capillaries* using the words from this list:

capillaries	out	thin	vessels	narrow	blood	cells

Capillaries are very *narrow* blood *vessels* with *thin* walls. Substances needed by the cells pass *out* of the *blood* through the capillary walls. Substances made by the *cells* can also pass into the blood through the walls of the *capillary.*

Q5 Which type of blood vessel is the one that gives us a pulse? *Artery*

Section Three — Human Biology Part One

Questions on The Blood

Q1 Match the type of blood cell to the correct description of its function

Blood cell	⟹	Function

red blood cells — help blood to clot at the site of a wound
platelets — transport oxygen from the lungs to the organs
white blood cells — ingest bacteria in the blood

(lines crossed: red blood cells → transport oxygen; platelets → help blood to clot; white blood cells → ingest bacteria)

Q2 a) Put a tick in the box next to each correct sentence about *plasma:*
- ☐ Plasma is a red coloured liquid.
- ☑ Plasma transports breakdown products of digestion.
- ☐ Plasma transports oxygen from the lungs to the organs.
- ☑ Plasma transports platelets.
- ☑ Plasma transports urea from the liver to the kidneys.

b) Two sentences are incorrect. Write down correct versions of them in the spaces below.

Plasma is pale straw coloured liquid
Red B. Cells transport ...

c) Plasma has other functions that are not listed in part a). Give another function of plasma.

Carries white & red blood cells

Q3 *Three components of the blood consist of cells or fragments of cells.*
a) Write down their names.

1 _White BC_   2 _Red BC_   3 _Platelets_

b) Only one of these components has a nucleus. Which one? _White BC_

c) The diagram on the right shows one of the cells named in part b). Write down the names of the parts labelled A, B and C.

Part A _Nucleus_

Part B _Cytoplasm_

Part C _Cell Membrane_

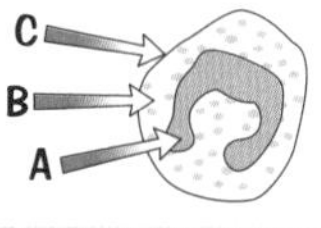

Q4 *Red cells have a shape called a biconcave disc (look at the diagram of a cut away red cell). This gives them a large surface area for their volume.*
a) Explain how this shape helps the red cell to do its job well.

Large surface area to vol. ratio allows lots of Oxygen absorption

b) The cytoplasm of red cells contains haemoglobin. What does haemoglobin do? _Bonds to oxygen_

c) Red cells in humans and most other mammals have no nucleus. Suggest a reason why.

To maximise volume for haemoglobin

34

Questions on Lungs and Breathing

Q1 In the sentences below circle the correct words in the underlined pairs.
a) The breathing system takes (air)/ oxygen into and out of the body.
b) This allows carbon dioxide /(oxygen)to pass from the air into the bloodstream.
c) It also allows(carbon dioxide)/ oxygen to pass out of the bloodstream into the air.

Q2 The diagram shows the *thorax.* Match up the parts with the correct labels.

Some parts will have more than one label.

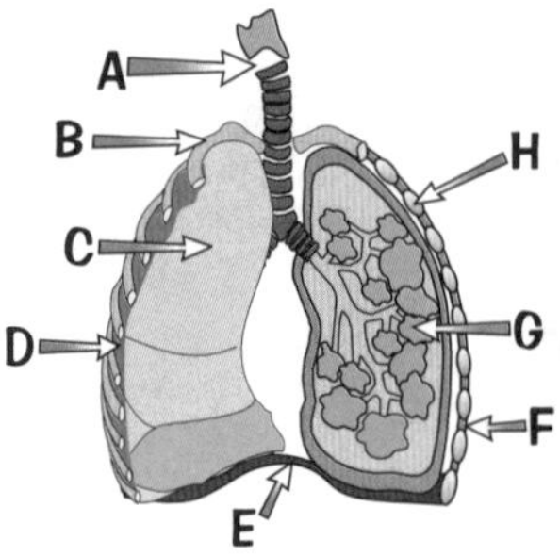

Name of part	label
alveoli	G
diaphragm	E
intercostal muscles	D / F
lung	C
ribs	H / B
trachea	A

Q3 *When air is breathed in through the nose or mouth, it passes through parts of the breathing system to the alveoli.*
Write down these parts of the breathing system in the correct order, starting at the nose:

bronchioles	trachea	bronchi	alveoli

Nose ⟹ _trachea_ ⟹ _bronchi_

alveoli ⟸ _bronchioles_

35

Questions on Lungs and Breathing

Q4 Match the part of the breathing system to its correct function.

Name of Part	⟹	Function

the ribcage — separates the lungs from the lower part of the body
the diaphragm — is the upper part of the body containing the lungs
the thorax — protects the lungs from damage

(lines crossed)

Q5 Complete the paragraph below using the words given.

oxygen	carbon dioxide	alveoli	alveolus	red

Each lung contains millions of tiny air sacs called _alveoli_ The alveoli are surrounded by a network of blood capillaries. At each _alveolus_ _oxygen_ passes into the blood and _carbon dioxide_ passes out of the blood. _Red_ blood cells carry the oxygen to all the cells in the body.

Q6 a) The *trachea* has rings of cartilage around it. What do these rings of cartilage do?

They stop the wind pipe collapsing when pressure inside is low.

b) The trachea splits into smaller air passages called *bronchi.* How many bronchi do each of us have?

Number of bronchi _2_

c) What is a bronchiole?

A small bronchus - next division of airways

d) What are the alveoli?

Air sacs where gaseous exchange occurs

36

Questions on Lungs and Breathing

Q7 *The air we breath out has a different composition to the air we breath in.*

Gas	% in inhaled air	% in exhaled air
oxygen	21	16
carbon dioxide	0.04	5
nitrogen	78	78

Complete the table above to show the percentages of oxygen, carbon dioxide and nitrogen in inhaled and exhaled air. Use the numbers from the box below.

0.04	21	78	16	5	78

Q8 The left hand side of the table below explains what happens when we breathe in. Complete the right hand side of the table to explain what happens when we breathe out. Use these words:

more	downwards	relax	decreases	up	relax	out

Breathing In	Breathing Out
The diaphragm muscles contract.	The diaphragm muscles _relax_.
This causes the diaphragm to flatten.	This causes the diaphragm to move upwards.
The muscles between the ribs contract.	The muscles between the ribs _relax_.
This pulls the ribcage upwards.	This pulls the ribcage _downwards_.
The volume of the thorax increases.	The volume of the thorax _decreases_.
The pressure inside the thorax goes down.	The pressure inside the thorax goes _up_.
The pressure inside the thorax gets less than atmospheric pressure.	The pressure inside the thorax gets _more_ than atmospheric pressure.
Air is pushed into the lungs from outside to make the pressures equal.	Air is pushed _out_ of the lungs to make the pressures equal.

Q9 Circle the correct words from the underlined pairs in the sentences below.

Gaseous exchange happens in the trachea /(alveoli.)

The cilia keep the lungs(clean)/ warm.

The mucous membranes make the air coming into the air passages dry /(moist)and (warm)/ cold.

Questions on Respiration

Q1 Complete the sentences below about respiration using the words from this list:

molecules	all	large	temperature	smaller	contract	plants

Respiration is a process that takes place in *all* living cells. Respiration transfers energy from food *molecules* in animals and *plants*. The energy from respiration is used to make *large* molecules from *smaller* ones, to let muscles *contract* and to keep a constant body *temperature*.

Q2 a) Put a tick in the box ☐ next to each correct sentence about respiration:

☐ Plants cannot respire.

☐ Respiration means getting air in and out of the lungs.

☑ Respiration releases energy from food molecules in cells.

b) Write down the correct versions of the sentences above that are wrong.

All living things respire.

Breathing means getting air in/out of lungs.

Q3 a) Complete the following word equation to describe respiration.

Glucose + *Oxygen* ⟹ *carbon dioxide* + water (+ energy).

b) Look at your equation. What two substances are needed for respiration?

Substance 1 *Glucose*

Substance 2 *Oxygen*

c) What two substances are produced by respiration?

Substance 1 *Carbon dioxide*

Substance 2 *Water*

Section Three — Human Biology Part One

Questions on Anaerobic Respiration

Q1 The word equation for *aerobic* respiration is:

glucose + oxygen ⟹ carbon dioxide + water (+ energy transferred)

In *anaerobic* respiration in humans, energy is released by converting glucose into lactic acid. No oxygen is needed for this to happen.

a) Write the word equation for anaerobic respiration in humans:

Glucose ⟹ *lactic acid + energy*

b) Aerobic respiration releases 16,000 J from 1g of glucose, and anaerobic respiration releases 833 J from 1g of glucose. Which process releases the most energy from glucose?

Aerobic

c) Write down one similarity, and one difference between aerobic and anaerobic respiration.

Similarity *Start with glucose / release energy*

Difference *Don't both use O_2 / Amount of energy released*

d) Why are the two types of respiration named aerobic and anaerobic?

Aerobic means using O_2 /air.

Anaerobic means without air.

Q2 Complete the sentences below about anaerobic respiration using the words from this list:

cramp	energy	shortage	oxygen
	lactic acid	poison	respiring

Anaerobic respiration in humans produces *energy* from glucose without needing *oxygen*. This means that when there is a *shortage* of oxygen, cells can carry on *respiring* for a short time.

Anaerobic respiration releases *lactic acid* as a waste. This is a mild *poison* and can cause *cramp*.

Section Three — Human Biology Part One

Questions on Anaerobic Respiration

Q3 *David does a simple experiment to investigate respiration and muscle activity.*

He rapidly clenches and unclenches his fist, counting how many times he can do this before his hand feels like it's going to fall off. His results are shown in the table on the right.

Number of clenches	
hand lowered	hand raised
201	82

Circle the correct words in each of the underlined pairs in the sentences below:

a) At the start of the experiment (aerobic) / anaerobic respiration was happening in his muscles.

b) At the end of the experiment, aerobic / (anaerobic) respiration was happening in his muscles.

c) During the experiment, (lactic acid) / carbon dioxide was made which caused cramp.

d) Why does it make a difference whether his hand is raised or lowered during the experiment?

It affects the blood flow to his hand.

Q4 The word equation for fermentation is:

glucose ⟹ alcohol + carbon dioxide (+ energy transferred).

Circle the correct words in each of the underlined pairs in the sentences below:

a) Fermentation is an example of aerobic / (anaerobic) respiration.

b) Yeast is a microscopic bacterium / (fungus) that can produce oxygen / (carbon dioxide) and water / (alcohol) from glucose by fermentation.

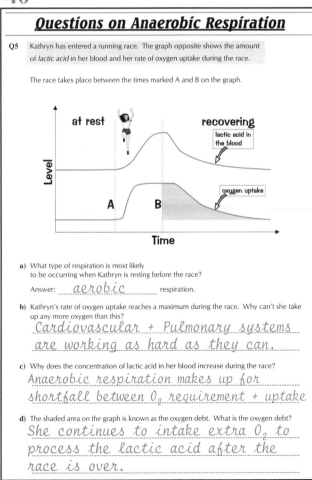

Section Three — Human Biology Part One

Questions on Anaerobic Respiration

Q5 Kathryn has entered a running race. The graph opposite shows the amount of *lactic acid* in her blood and her rate of oxygen uptake during the race.

The race takes place between the times marked A and B on the graph.

at rest / recovering

lactic acid in the blood

Level

A   B

oxygen uptake

Time

a) What type of respiration is most likely to be occurring when Kathryn is resting before the race?

Answer: *aerobic* respiration.

b) Kathryn's rate of oxygen uptake reaches a maximum during the race. Why can't she take up any more oxygen than this?

Cardiovascular + Pulmonary systems are working as hard as they can.

c) Why does the concentration of lactic acid in her blood increase during the race?

Anaerobic respiration makes up for shortfall between O_2 requirement + uptake

d) The shaded area on the graph is known as the oxygen debt. What is the oxygen debt?

She continues to intake extra O_2 to process the lactic acid after the race is over.

Section Three — Human Biology Part One

Questions on The Nervous System

Q1 a) Put a tick in the box next to each correct sentence about the nervous system:

- ☑ Receptors are cells which can detect changes in the environment.
- ☑ A stimulus is a change in the environment.
- ☑ There are receptors in the ear which are sensitive to changes in position.
- ☐ Nerve impulses pass from the brain to the receptors.

b) The sentence without a tick is incorrect. Write down a correct version of it in the space below.

Nerve Imp. pass from receptors to brain.

Q2 Match up the following sense organs with the receptors they contain.

Organs → Receptors

- eyes have receptors
- ears have receptors
- tongue and nose have receptors
- skin have receptors

- that are sensitive to pressure and temperature
- that are sensitive to light
- that are sensitive to chemicals
- that are sensitive to sound and changes in position

Q3 Complete the sentences below using the words from this list:

see	skin	pressure	taste	nose	hear	balance

The eye is the organ which allows us to *see*. The *skin* is the organ which gives us the sense of touch by responding to changes in *pressure*

The tongue gives us the sense of *taste* and the *nose* allows us to smell things. The ears are important because they allow us to *hear* and keep our *balance*.

Q4 The diagram on the right shows the main features of the nervous system.

a) Name the parts of the nervous system labelled **X**, **Y** and **Z**.

X : *brain*   Y: *spinal column*

Z: *neurones*

b) When parts **X** and **Y** are taken together, they have a name. What is this name?

Name of parts X and Y together: *central nervous system*

c) In which direction can nerve impulses travel in the part labelled **Y**?
Circle the correct answer from the three choices below:

i) From the brain only   ii) To the brain only   iii) Both to and from the brain

Section Three — Human Biology Part One

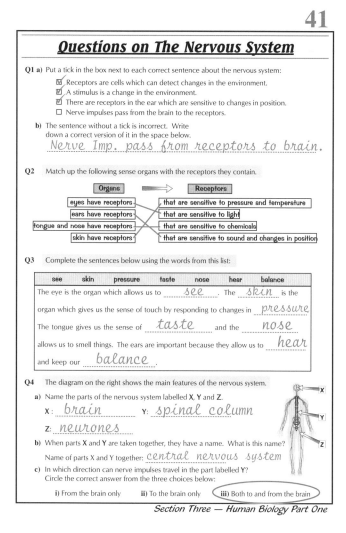

Questions on The Nervous System

Q5 When some grit gets in your eye, your eye begins to water. This is a reflex action. The grit irritates the eye, and is the stimulus. The eyes watering is the response.

a) Write down another example of a reflex action.

Eg Snatching your hand away from fire

b) Name the stimulus, and the response, in this reflex action.

Stimulus *Eg fire*   Response *Eg movement*

Q6 Circle the correct words from each underlined pair in the sentences below:

A reflex action is a conscious / an automatic response. It is a response to a stimulus / receptor.
Reflex actions happen very quickly / slowly. They involve / do not involve the brain / Brian.
Reflex actions are considered / emergency reactions.

Q9 Complete these sentences about neurones.

Choose from the list of words below. You can use words more than once, if you need to.

receptor	effector	spinal cord

a) Sensory neurones carry nerve impulses from the *receptor* to the *spinal cord*

b) Motor neurones carry nerve impulses from the *spinal cord* to the *effector*

Q10 The spinal cord can be damaged from an accident or an illness. As a result, the person may be unable to feel anything below the damaged part of the spinal cord.

Explain why this happens.
Nerve connections have been broken, so nerve impulses cannot be passed to the brain.

Section Three — Human Biology Part One

Questions on The Eye

Q1 Look at the diagram below. It shows a section through an eye.
— Label the different parts A to K, in the spaces provided.

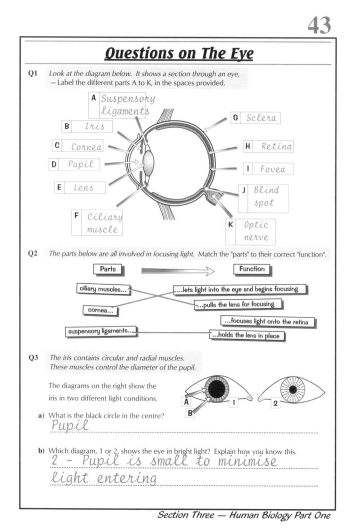

A *Suspensory ligaments*
B *Iris*
C *Cornea*
D *Pupil*
E *Lens*
F *Ciliary muscle*
G *Sclera*
H *Retina*
I *Fovea*
J *Blind spot*
K *Optic nerve*

Q2 The parts below are all involved in focusing light. Match the "parts" to their correct "function".

Parts → Function

- ciliary muscles...
- cornea...
- suspensory ligaments...

- ...lets light into the eye and begins focusing
- ...pulls the lens for focusing
- ...focuses light onto the retina
- ...holds the lens in place

Q3 The iris contains circular and radial muscles. These muscles control the diameter of the pupil.

The diagrams on the right show the iris in two different light conditions.

a) What is the black circle in the centre?
Pupil

b) Which diagram, 1 or 2, shows the eye in bright light? Explain how you know this.
2 - Pupil is small to minimise light entering

Section Three — Human Biology Part One

Questions on the Use of Hormones

Q1 Complete the diagram below to show how hormones travel from a gland, causing a response in a target organ.

Choose from the list of words below:

endocrine gland	hormone	bloodstream	response	target organ

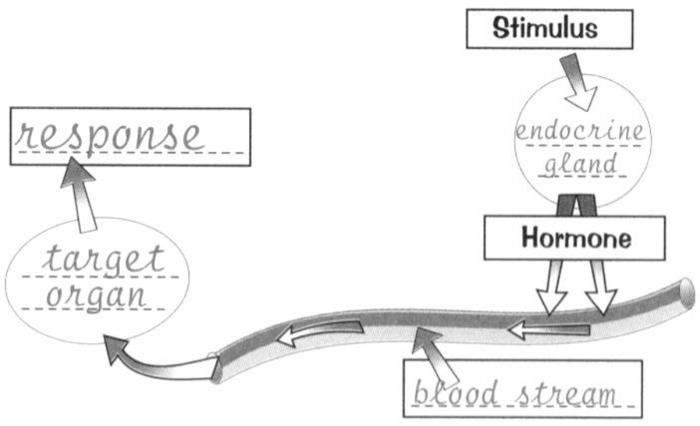

response   Stimulus   *endocrine gland*

target organ   Hormone

blood stream

Q2 Hormones are important in controlling the level of sugar in the blood. One hormone reduces the amount of sugar in the blood, and the other hormone increases it. Study the diagram below and answer the questions.

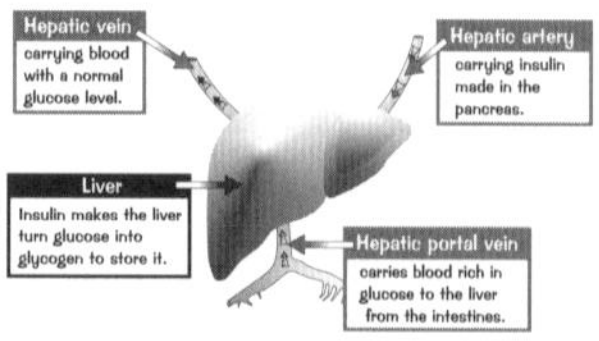

a) Name the hormone in the diagram.
Insulin

b) Where is this hormone made?
Pancreas

c) Name the target organ for this hormone.
Liver

Hepatic vein — carrying blood with a normal glucose level.
Hepatic artery — carrying blood made in the pancreas.
Liver — Insulin makes the liver turn glucose into glycogen to store it.
Hepatic portal vein — carries blood rich in glucose to the liver from the intestines.

d) Does this hormone cause the level of glucose in the blood to go up or down? *down*

e) Use your answers to complete these sentences about the amount of sugar in blood:

A hormone called *insulin* is made in the *pancreas*.
This hormone is transported by the bloodstream to its target organ, which is the *liver*. Here, glucose is turned into *glycogen* which *reduces* the amount of sugar.

Section Four — Human Biology Part Two

45

Questions on the Use of Hormones

Q3 Complete the sentences below about hormones using the words from this list:

target	glands	processes	bloodstream	co-ordinated	chemicals

Many *processes* in the body are *co-ordinated* by hormones.

Hormones are *chemicals* They are produced by *glands*.

Hormones are transported to their *target* organs by the *boodstream*

Q5 *Diabetes is a disease in which the pancreas does not produce enough insulin.*

a) What will happen to the level of sugar in the blood if enough insulin is not produced?

It will rise.

b) Why do people with diabetes need to pay careful attention to their diet?

They don't produce enough insulin, so if they eat too much sugar they'll get ill.

c) *Diabetes can be treated by injecting insulin into the bloodstream.* What will this do?

It will reduce the level of sugar in the blood.

46

Questions on Hormones and Fertility

Q1 *The lining of a woman's uterus changes in thickness in a monthly cycle, ready to receive an egg.*

a) What is this monthly cycle called? *menstrual cycle*

The diagram on the right shows these changes in thickness during a 28 day cycle. Study the diagram, then answer these questions:

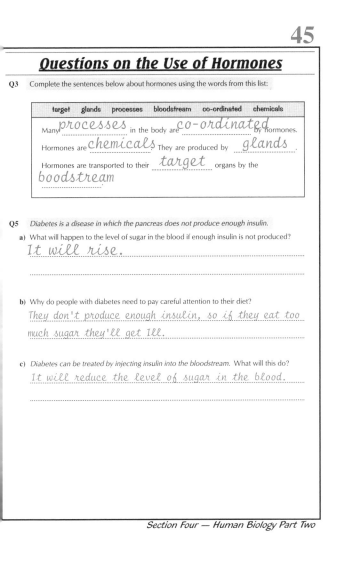

b) When is the lining of the uterus thickest? Between day *14* and day *21*

c) An egg is released from the ovary on day 14. Suggest an advantage of releasing an egg then.

The lining of the uterus is in good condition to receive it if the egg is fertilised

d) Circle the correct name for the monthly loss of blood: ovulation/**menstruation**/micrition.

Q2 Match the descriptions below to the correct term. One has been done for you.

Description	Term
Eggs are released from the organs called	menstruation
The hormone that controls the uterus lining thickness is made in	ovulation
The monthly loss of the uterus lining is called	the ovaries
The monthly release of an egg is called	

Q3 Name a place where hormones are made that control the female reproductive system.

Ovaries

Q4 Write down two events in the menstrual cycle that are controlled by hormones.

a) *Growth of uterus lining (break down of lining)* **b)** *Release of egg (maintenance of lining)*

Q5 *Women's fertility can be controlled using manufactured hormones.*
Circle the correct word in each of the underlined pairs in the sentences below:

a) A woman's fertility (increases)/ decreases if she is given hormones that stimulate egg release.

b) A woman's fertility increases /(decreases) if she is given hormones that prevent egg release.

Questions on Hormones and Fertility

Q6 Write down one advantage of using manufactured hormones to control fertility in women, and one disadvantage of doing this.

Advantage: *Family planning facilated, levels of infertility reduced*

Disadvantage: *Health risks (cancer, thrombosis) excessive number of babies (octuplets etc), higher risk of HIV than with condoms*

Q7 Solve the Hormones Wordsearch.

Words to find:

bloodstream	chemicals	endocrine	gland	glucagon
hormone	insulin	liver	oestrogen	
ovaries	pancreas	pituitary	testosterone	uterus

```
          T W Z T
  G O     I E Y Z X D
H L E O D R O F S Q J P M U
B O U S M V Q N L T G L A N D
J B R C T H W A A R O M E J R W
D A M A R G L C R U S R R C L S
B Q O G C P I T U I T A R Y A
E R N O G M V U I S E E T E M
  E N E V E W D L R S R A
  Z H N B R O I X O C Z U V
G C E N D O C R I N E P J S O
I N S U L I N S A E F X F R J
L K W B A P J P R Z P C U W
  I F E P G R   R D D J I
      A I E Q     M B
```

Questions on Disease in Humans

Q1 *The two main types of microbes that can cause disease are bacteria and viruses. Write down the name of each type of microbe shown in the pictures below. (the pictures are not drawn to scale).*

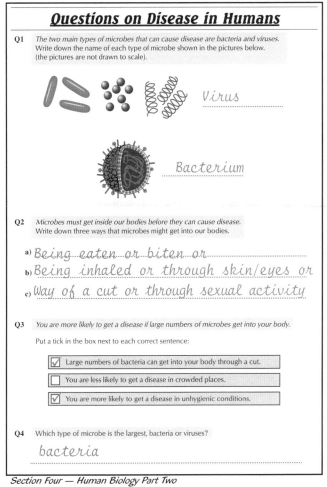

Virus

Bacterium

Q2 *Microbes must get inside our bodies before they can cause disease. Write down three ways that microbes might get into our bodies.*

a) *Being eaten or biten or*

b) *Being inhaled or through skin/eyes or*

c) *Way of a cut or through sexual activity*

Q3 *You are more likely to get a disease if large numbers of microbes get into your body.*

Put a tick in the box next to each correct sentence:

- ☑ Large numbers of bacteria can get into your body through a cut.
- ☐ You are less likely to get a disease in crowded places.
- ☑ You are more likely to get a disease in unhygienic conditions.

Q4 Which type of microbe is the largest, bacteria or viruses?

bacteria

Questions on Disease in Humans

Q5 Write down two ways in which bacteria or viruses can be passed from one person to another.

a) *droplets of water in sneezes or STDs or contamination of food or water or*

b) *physical contact or insects could bite one person and then bite another.*

Q6 When bacteria and viruses grow in our bodies, they can produce chemicals called toxins. Write down another name for these chemicals.

Name: *Poisons*

Q7 When viruses reproduce in a cell, they break out of the cell in large numbers and infect other cells. Circle the correct words from each of the underlined pairs in the sentences below:

Viruses escape from an infected cell through the cell's *nucleus* / (*membrane*).

When viruses escape from an infected cell, they (*do*) / *do not* damage the cell.

Viruses (*do*) / *do not* need to reproduce inside living cells.

Q8 Complete the sentences below about microbes and disease using the words from this list:

genes	protein	microbes	toxins	rapidly	smaller	nucleus

Diseases can be caused when *microbes* get into the body. Bacteria and viruses reproduce *rapidly* inside the body. They produce *toxins* which make us feel ill. Viruses are *smaller* than bacteria, and consist of a *protein* coat with a few genes inside. Bacteria have *genes* but they are not in a *nucleus*.

Q9 In Japan, people with a cold often wear a mask over their mouth and nose when they go outside.

Suggest a reason why they do this. *To avoid infecting others*

50

Questions on Fighting Disease

Q1 Microbes must get into the body before they can cause disease. Our bodies have several natural defences that can stop microbes getting in. Match the natural defence to the correct part of the body:

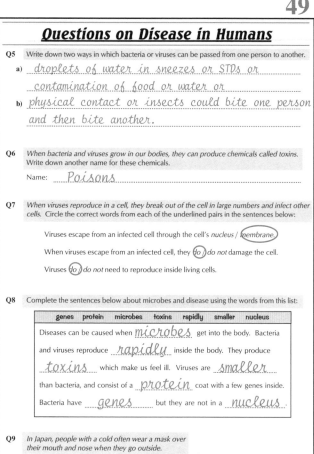

natural defence ⟹ part of the body

- hydrochloric acid is produced to kill microbes — skin
- acts as a barrier to microbes — stomach
- a sticky liquid is produced to trap microbes — blood
- clots are produced to seal cuts — breathing organs

Q2 Cells in the blood can defend the body against microbes if they manage to get past the natural defences. The diagrams below show cells that are found in blood. Write down the name of each type of cell in the spaces. Choose from these labels:

red cell   white cell

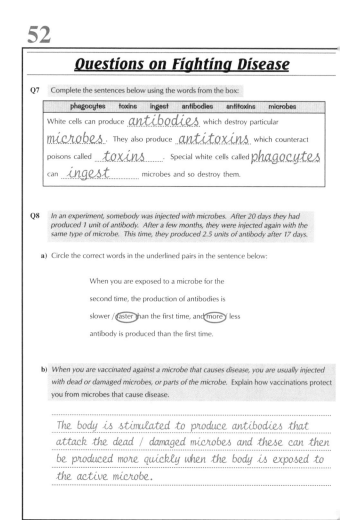

White cell

Red cell

Q3 White cells help to defend the body against microbes that cause disease.

What do the red cells do?

They carry oxygen around the body

51

Questions on Fighting Disease

Q5 At each stage in getting a disease caused by a microbe, the body has defences. For each of the stages below, write down an example of the body's defence against microbes:

Bacteria getting into a cut: *Blood clotting seals wound. White blood cells attack microbes that enter blood.*

Bacteria producing toxins: *White blood cells produce antitoxins. The liver processes toxins*

Bacteria being breathed in: *Sticky mucus / hairs in air ways traps bacteria before they enter bloodstream.*

Q6 Look at the diagram on the right, then write down below how each of the parts **A** to **D** can protect the body against microbes.

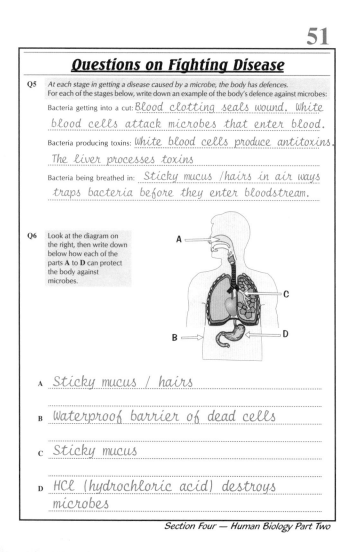

A *Sticky mucus / hairs*

B *Waterproof barrier of dead cells*

C *Sticky mucus*

D *HCl (hydrochloric acid) destroys microbes*

Questions on Fighting Disease

Q7 Complete the sentences below using the words from the box:

phagocytes	toxins	ingest	antibodies	antitoxins	microbes

White cells can produce *antibodies* which destroy particular *microbes*. They also produce *antitoxins* which counteract poisons called *toxins*. Special white cells called *phagocytes* can *ingest* microbes and so destroy them.

Q8 In an experiment, somebody was injected with microbes. After 20 days they had produced 1 unit of antibody. After a few months, they were injected again with the same type of microbe. This time, they produced 2.5 units of antibody after 17 days.

a) Circle the correct words in the underlined pairs in the sentence below:

When you are exposed to a microbe for the second time, the production of antibodies is *slower* / (*faster*) than the first time, and (*more*) / *less* antibody is produced than the first time.

b) When you are vaccinated against a microbe that causes disease, you are usually injected with dead or damaged microbes, or parts of the microbe. Explain how vaccinations protect you from microbes that cause disease.

The body is stimulated to produce antibodies that attack the dead / damaged microbes and these can then be produced more quickly when the body is exposed to the active microbe.

Questions on Drugs

Q1 a) Match the substances below to the correct descriptions.

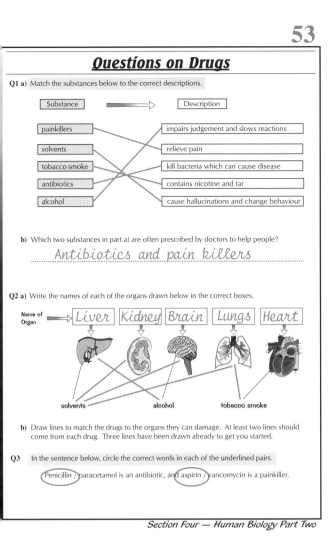

Substance		Description
painkillers		impairs judgement and slows reactions
solvents		relieve pain
tobacco smoke		kill bacteria which can cause disease
antibiotics		contains nicotine and tar
alcohol		cause hallucinations and change behaviour

b) Which two substances in part a) are often prescribed by doctors to help people?

Antibiotics and pain killers

Q2 a) Write the names of each of the organs drawn below in the correct boxes.

Name of Organs → *Liver* *Kidney* *Brain* *Lungs* *Heart*

solvents   alcohol   tobacco smoke

b) Draw lines to match the drugs to the organs they can damage. At least two lines should come from each drug. Three lines have been drawn already to get you started.

Q3 In the sentence below, circle the correct words in each of the underlined pairs.

(Penicillin) / paracetamol is an antibiotic, and aspirin / (vancomycin) is a painkiller.

Questions on Drugs

Q4 Complete the sentences below about drugs using the words from this list:

addicted	processes	chemicals	ill	helpful	withdrawal

Drugs are *chemicals* which change the way the body works.

Some are *helpful* to *ill* people, but

others change the chemical *processes* in people's bodies.

These changes can make people *addicted* them and suffer

from *withdrawal* symptoms if they stop taking the drug.

Q5 a) Put a tick in the box next to each of the correct sentences about alcohol:

- [ ] Alcohol speeds up reactions and can lead to lack of self-control.
- [x] Too much alcohol can lead to unconsciousness and coma.
- [x] Alcohol can cause damage to liver and brain cells.

Q6 Study the diagram below, then answer the questions.
One unit of alcohol is 10cm³ of alcohol.

½ pint of beer contains approx. 10cm³ of alcohol = glass of wine = glass of sherry = single measure of spirits

a) How many units are there in ½ pint of beer?

1 Units.

b) How many units are there in a double measure of spirits?

2 Units.

55

Questions on Drugs

c) A person at a party drinks a pint of beer, 3 glasses of wine, and two double whiskies (a spirit). How many units of alcohol has he drunk? Show your working out.

1 pt beer = 2 units, 3 gls wine = 3 units, 2 dbls = 4 untis. Total 2 + 3 + 4 = 9 units

d) Why would it be unsafe for the person in part c) to drive home after the party?

Their reactions would be very slow and coordination would be impaired. Also lack of inhibition could lead to reckless driving.

Q7 Circle the correct words in each of the underlined pairs in these sentences about tobacco smoke:

1) (Tar) / nicotine is the substance in tobacco smoke that can cause lung cancer.

2) The substance in tobacco smoke that causes addiction is carbon monoxide / (nicotine).

Q8 The table below shows the effects on the body of three common drugs.

Complete the table using the words in the box. Some words can be used more than once. Put a tick in the last row if the substance is addictive.

Liver	Heart	Kidneys	Hallucinations
Slows reactions		Emphysema	Brain

	alcohol	tobacco	solvents
organs damaged	Brain and *Liver*	Lungs and *Heart*	*Brain* *Liver* *Kidneys*
effect on the body	*Slows reactions*	Lung cancer and *Emphysema*	*Hallucinations*
addictive?	✓	✓	*No*

Questions on Homeostasis

Q1 The graph below shows the results of an experiment into the effects on the body of increasing the air temperature. The squares show the volume of urine produced per hour. The circles show the volume of sweat produced per hour.

a) Circle the correct words in each underlined pair:

As the temperature goes up, the volume of

urine produced goes up / (down), and the

volume of sweat produced goes (up) / down.

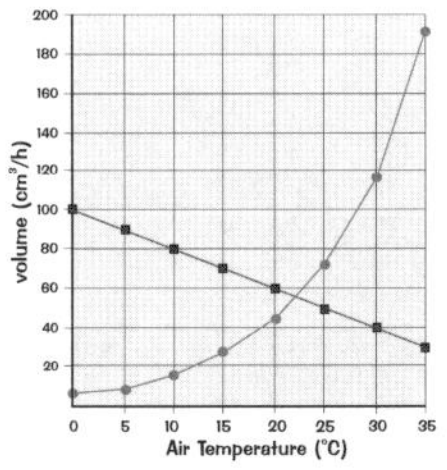

b) At which temperature is the volume of urine produced the same as the volume of sweat?

Temperature = *22* °C

c) Why do we feel more thirsty in hot weather? *Our bodies lose water maintaining temperature and tells us to make up the loss by making us feel thirsty.*

Q2 Match the method of water loss to the correct organ in the body:

Method of water loss		Organ
water is lost by sweating through the		kidneys
water is lost by breathing using the		skin
water is lost as urine made in the		lungs

Q3 In an experiment, 10 members of a class took their temperatures. Their results are shown below:

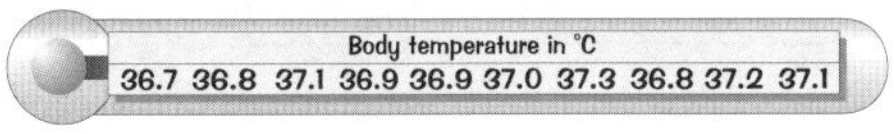

Body temperature in °C
36.7 36.8 37.1 36.9 36.9 37.0 37.3 36.8 37.2 37.1

a) Work out the average body temperature for these 10 students. Show your working out.

[36.7 + 36.8 ÷ 10] *37.0* °C

b) What is normal human body temperature? *37* °C

Questions on Homeostasis

Q4 *For us to stay healthy, the temperature of the body must be maintained at the temperature that enzymes work best. The table below shows how the temperature of a human body and a reptile's body changes during the day in a hot climate.*

Time	4 a.m	8 a.m	12 noon	4 p.m	8 p.m	midnight
Air Temperature (°C)	10	22	39	39	30	8
Human body temperature (°C)	37	37	37	37	37	37
Reptile body temperature (°C)	7	19	10	10	19	7

a) Between which times is the air temperature highest? Between __12__ and __4pm__.

b) The reptile goes underground when the air temperature is highest. Why does it do this?
To keep its body temperature from getting too high.

c) What happens to the human's body temperature during the day? *constant*

d) Circle the correct words in each of the underlined pairs in the sentences below:

1. Reptiles can / (cannot) use energy from respiration to maintain their body temperature.

2. Humans (can) / cannot use energy from respiration to maintain their body temperature.

3. Humans maintain their body temperature by sweating when the air temperature gets low / (high.)

Q5 *The amount of sugar in the blood must be kept at a constant level for us to stay healthy.*

a) Name the two hormones involved in keeping the blood sugar level constant.

Hormone 1 __Insulin__   Hormone 2 __Glucagon__

b) *In a certain disease, one of these hormones is only produced in small amounts, and the blood sugar level might rise to fatal levels. Name the disease and the hormone involved.*

Name of disease __Diabetes__   Name of hormone __Insulin__

Section Four — Human Biology Part Two

58

Questions on Skin

Q1 *If we get embarrassed or too hot, our skin goes red. This is because the capillaries in the skin get wider and let more blood through.*

Circle the correct words in the underlined pairs in the sentences below about the skin:

a) When the capillaries get wider, this is called vasoconstriction / (vasodilation.)

b) When we get cold (less) / more blood goes through our skin, and our skin looks (blue) / red.

c) When we get cold, our hairs (stand up) / lie down to trap a layer of warm air near the skin.

Q2 Complete the flow chart to show how the skin helps us maintain a constant body temperature. Use the words in the box below.

more sweat	get narrower	stand up
less sweat	get wider	lie down

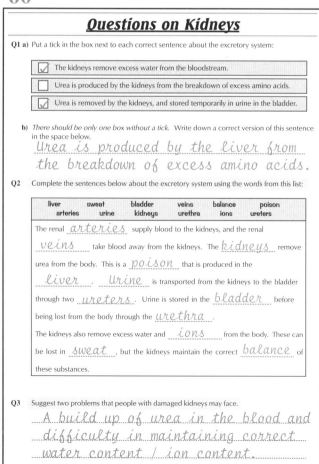

falling body temperature ← normal body temperature → rising body temperature

less sweat

more sweat

sweating

stand up

lie down

hairs

get narrower

get wider

capillaries

normal body temperature

Section Four — Human Biology Part Two

59

Questions on Skin

Q3 Complete the sentences below about the skin, using the words from the box:

vasoconstriction	lie down	capillaries	hairs	blood	narrower

When the body gets too cold, the *capillaries* in our skin get *narrower* and let less *blood* through. This is called *vasoconstriction*. When we get too hot, the *hairs* on our skin *lie down* to let heat escape from the skin.

Q4 *The skin is the largest organ of the body. It plays important roles in keeping the body free from disease and protecting our internal organs.*

a) How does the skin protect us from disease?
It is a waterproof barrier and the outer layer is dead.

b) Why does having waterproof skin protect you from microbes?
Many microbes exist in dirty water that could enter our bodies if skin was not waterproof.

Q5 *We sweat to help maintain a constant body temperature. Sweat contains water and salts.*

a) Put a tick in the box next to each correct sentence:

- ☑ Water also leaves the body in urine.
- ☐ Water also leaves the body through the lungs when we breathe in.
- ☑ Salts also leave the body in urine.

b) *There should be only one box without a tick. Write down a correct version of this sentence in the space below.*
Water also leaves through the lungs when we breathe out.

Section Four — Human Biology Part Two

Questions on Kidneys

Q1 a) Put a tick in the box next to each correct sentence about the excretory system:

- ☑ The kidneys remove excess water from the bloodstream.
- ☐ Urea is produced by the kidneys from the breakdown of excess amino acids.
- ☑ Urea is removed by the kidneys, and stored temporarily in urine in the bladder.

b) *There should be only one box without a tick. Write down a correct version of this sentence in the space below.*
Urea is produced by the liver from the breakdown of excess amino acids.

Q2 Complete the sentences below about the excretory system using the words from this list:

liver	sweat	bladder	veins	balance	poison
arteries	urine	kidneys	urethra	ions	ureters

The renal *arteries* supply blood to the kidneys, and the renal *veins* take blood away from the kidneys. The *kidneys* remove urea from the body. This is a *poison* that is produced in the *liver*. *Urine* is transported from the kidneys to the bladder through two *ureters*. Urine is stored in the *bladder* before being lost from the body through the *urethra*.

The kidneys also remove excess water and *ions* from the body. These can be lost in *sweat*, but the kidneys maintain the correct *balance* of these substances.

Q3 Suggest two problems that people with damaged kidneys may face.
A build up of urea in the blood and difficulty in maintaining correct water content / ion content.

Section Four — Human Biology Part Two

Questions on Variation

Q1 Individual animals and plants of the same species are usually not identical. They have different characteristics from each other, and show variation. Match the **description** to the correct **meaning**:

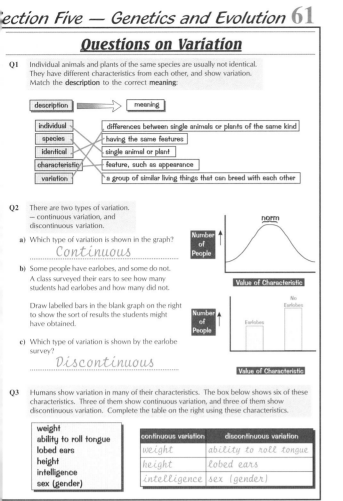

description → meaning

description	meaning
individual	differences between single animals or plants of the same kind
species	having the same features
identical	single animal or plant
characteristic	feature, such as appearance
variation	a group of similar living things that can breed with each other

Q2 There are two types of variation — continuous variation, and discontinuous variation.

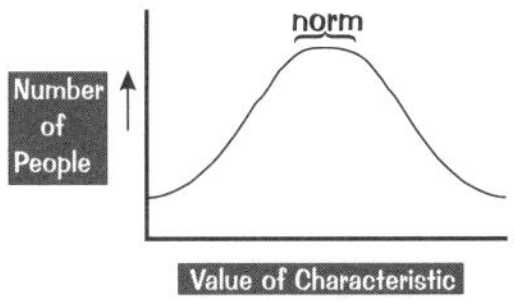

norm
Number of People
Value of Characteristic

a) Which type of variation is shown in the graph? Continuous

b) Some people have earlobes, and some do not. A class surveyed their ears to see how many students had earlobes and how many did not.

Draw labelled bars in the blank graph on the right to show the sort of results the students might have obtained.

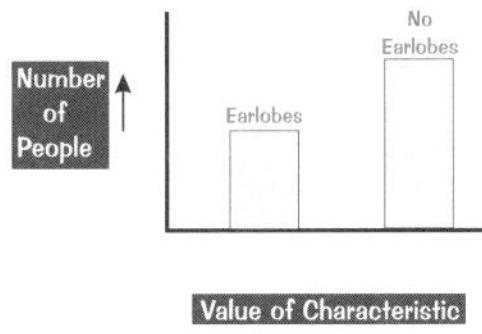

Number of People
Earlobes
No Earlobes
Value of Characteristic

c) Which type of variation is shown by the earlobe survey? Discontinuous

Q3 Humans show variation in many of their characteristics. The box below shows six of these characteristics. Three of them show continuous variation, and three of them show discontinuous variation. Complete the table on the right using these characteristics.

weight
ability to roll tongue
lobed ears
height
intelligence
sex (gender)

continuous variation	discontinuous variation
weight	ability to roll tongue
height	lobed ears
intelligence	sex (gender)

Questions on Variation

Q4 People belong to one of four main blood groups, A, B, AB, or O.

Complete the sentences below about blood groups using the words from this list:

group discontinuous categories four variation

There are four main blood groups. The variation in these blood groups is discontinuous. This is because there are distinct categories of blood group.

Q5 Animals and plants look similar to their parents because of information passed onto them by their parents. Genes carry this information. Variation between individuals can be due to differences in the genes they have inherited, to differences in the conditions around them, or both.

Complete the sentences below by circling the correct word in each of the brackets.

Differences in the (genes / conditions) produce variation due to genetic causes.

Variation caused by the (environment / genes) is due to differences in conditions.

A mixture of genetic and environmental differences (can / cannot) cause variation.

Q6 Identical twins have the same genes and are said to be genetically identical.

The table below shows the characteristics of four people, code-named M, Q, X, and Z.

Characteristic	Code-name M	Q	X	Z
They have a sun tan	✓	✓		
They are male	✓	✓	✓	
They are female				✓
They can roll their tongue	✓		✓	
Natural hair colour is brown	✓	✓	✓	✓
They have bleached white hair			✓	✓
They have brown eyes	✓	✓	✓	

a) Which people are male?

Code-names: M, Q and X

b) Who can roll their tongue and has a sun tan? Code-name: M

c) Which two features are caused by differences in the environment?

1 Having a sun tan   Having bleached white hair

d) Which two people must be the identical twins? Code-names: M and X

Questions on Variation

Q7 When Ayesha looked at the ivy plant growing up the tree in her back garden, she was surprised by how much the size and colour of the leaves varied.

a) What kind of variation is this, genetic or environmental? environmental

b) All mature ivy leaves have the same shape.

Is leaf shape determined genetically or environmentally? genetically

c) Is the size of the leaves a continuous or discontinuous variation?

Leaf size is a continuous variation.

Q8 Azra took geranium cuttings from one of the plants in her garden and gave half of them to her friend Andrew. Each grew their cuttings in their own gardens and a year later compared the growth of the plants and were amazed to see how differently the geraniums had grown.

The table shows what each set of plants looked like.

	Azra's plants	Andrew's plants
Leaves	Dark green, no spots	Pale green, brown spots
Stems	Tall and thick	Short and thin
Flowers	Large	Short and Thin

a) Suggest two things that could affect the appearance of the geranium plants.

1 The amount sunlight available / water available

2 The quality (nutrition available) of the soil

b) Do you think that the differences in their plants are due to environmental variations or genetic variations? Environmental variations

c) Give one reason for your answer to part b).

Cuttings are clones so all the geraniums were genetically identical. The differences must have been environmental

d) Circle the correct words in each of the brackets to complete the sentences below:

"All the flowers were orange" — This is due to (environmental / genetic) causes.

"The flowers were lots of different shades" — This is (continuous / discontinuous) variation.

"The plants are all of different heights" — This is (continuous / discontinuous) variation and is due to (environmental / genetic) causes.

Questions on Genes, Chromosomes and DNA

Q1 Read the information in the box, then answer the questions.

DNA is a chemical found in the nucleus of cells.

DNA is very long, so it is usually folded up into shapes called chromosomes to fit into the nucleus.

A gene is a section of DNA which has the information needed to control a particular characteristic.

a) Where do you find DNA? In the nucleus of a cell

b) Why is DNA made into chromosomes? Because it is too long to fit into the nucleus otherwise

c) What do we call a section of DNA that controls a particular characteristic? A gene

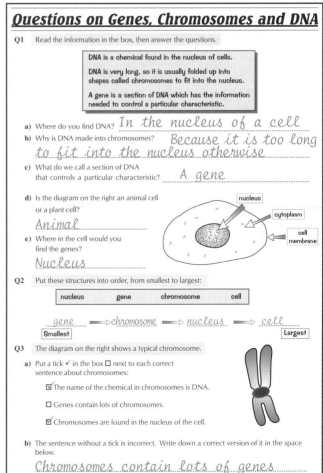

d) Is the diagram on the right an animal cell or a plant cell?

Animal

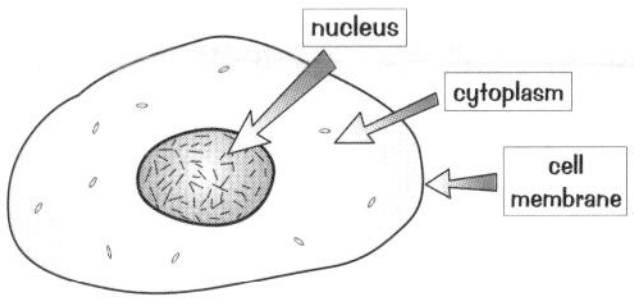

nucleus
cytoplasm
cell membrane

e) Where in the cell would you find the genes?

Nucleus

Q2 Put these structures into order, from smallest to largest:

nucleus gene chromosome cell

gene → chromosome → nucleus → cell

Smallest … Largest

Q3 The diagram on the right shows a typical chromosome.

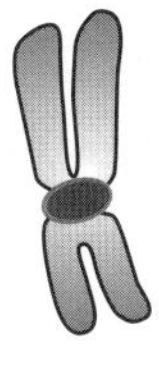

a) Put a tick ✓ in the box ☐ next to each correct sentence about chromosomes:

☑ The name of the chemical in chromosomes is DNA.

☐ Genes contain lots of chromosomes.

☑ Chromosomes are found in the nucleus of the cell.

b) The sentence without a tick is incorrect. Write down a correct version of it in the space below.

Chromosomes contain lots of genes

Questions on Genes, Chromosomes and DNA

Q4 An experiment was done with two fertilised frog eggs. The eggs came from completely different parents. The nucleus of egg A was put into egg B, and the nucleus of egg B was removed (see the diagram on the right).

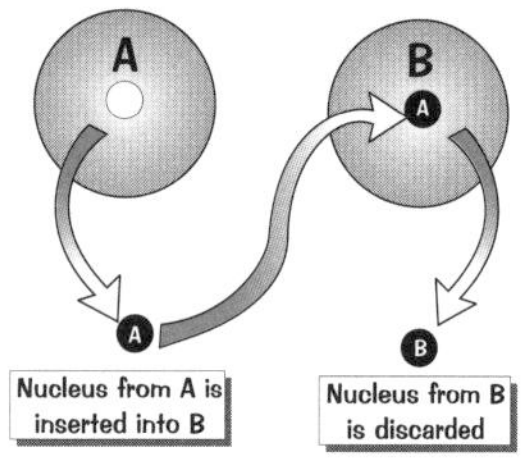

Nucleus from A is inserted into B

Nucleus from B is discarded

a) Egg **A** did not grow into a frog. Why not?

It had no nucleus so no genetic information

b) Egg **B** grew into a frog, but it looked like the parents of egg **A**, not the parents of egg **B**. Why was this?

Egg B had the genetic information of egg A's parents

Q5 The diagrams below show the chromosomes in each body cell of a man and a woman.

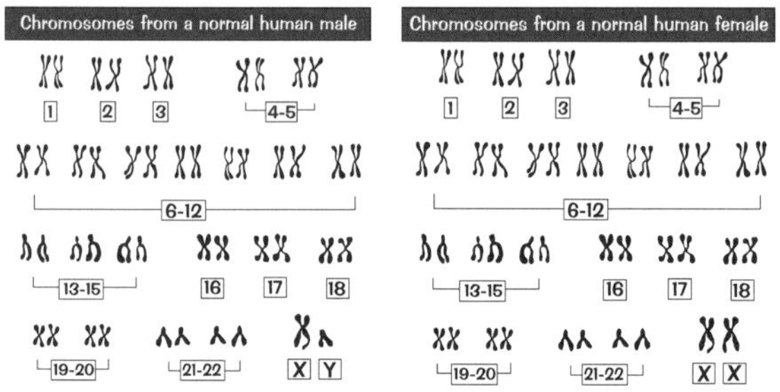

Chromosomes from a normal human male	Chromosomes from a normal human female

a) The chromosomes are found in pairs.
How many pairs of chromosomes are there in each cell?

Number of pairs of chromosomes: *23*

b) How many chromosomes are there altogether in each human body cell? *46*

c) What is the difference between the two sets of chromosomes?

In the male the 23rd pair is XY. For the female it is XX.

Section Five — Genetics and Evolution

Questions on Asexual Reproduction

Q1 There are two types of reproduction, asexual reproduction and sexual reproduction. Complete the table below with the sentences in the box to show the differences between asexual and sexual reproduction.

> Male and female sex cells join.
> Offspring are not genetically identical to parents.
> No joining of cells needed.
> Two parents are needed
> Offspring are genetically identical to parent.
> Only one parent is needed.

Asexual reproduction	Sexual reproduction
No joining of cells needed	*male and female sex cells join*
Only one parent is needed	*Two parents are needed*
Offspring are genetically identical to parent	*Offspring are not genetically identical to parents*

Q2 Genetically identical individuals are called clones. Gardeners can produce clones by taking "cuttings" from one plant. If they are kept in a damp atmosphere or in moist compost, the cuttings eventually grow roots and become a new plant (see diagram).

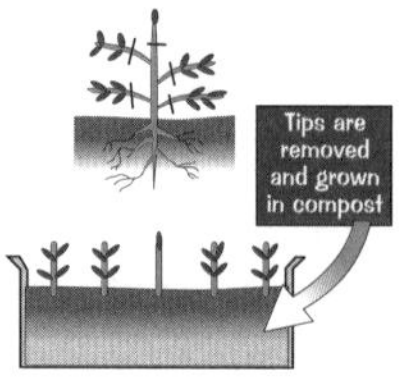

Tips are removed and grown in compost

a) Complete the following sentence:

Clones are *genetically identical* organisms.

b) What type of reproduction is involved in this method?

Asexual reproduction

c) Why are the new plants called clones?

Because they are genetically identical to each other and the parent.

d) Why would a gardener want to take cuttings from a plant that produces prize-winning flowers?

To grow identical prize-winning plants.

Section Five — Genetics and Evolution

Questions on Asexual Reproduction

Q3 Unlike humans, many plants reproduce asexually.

a) Give three examples of plants which reproduce asexually.

Example 1 *Strawberry plants*

Example 2 *Potato plants*

Example 3 *Daffodils*

examples

b) For one of the examples above say how the plant actually carries out asexual reproduction.

E.g. Strawberry plants grow runners

Strawberry plants can reproduce in two ways. They can use flowers, and they can also use runners.

c) Put a tick ✓ in the box ☐ next to each correct sentence about reproduction in strawberry plants:

☑ Asexual reproduction involves runners.

☑ Flowers are needed for strawberry fruits to form.

☐ Seeds produce new plants that are genetically identical to each other.

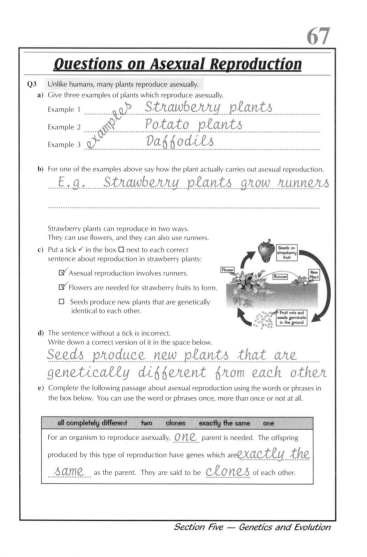

Seeds on strawberry fruit

Flower

Runner

New Plant

Fruit rots and seeds germinate in the ground

d) The sentence without a tick is incorrect. Write down a correct version of it in the space below.

Seeds produce new plants that are genetically different from each other

e) Complete the following passage about asexual reproduction using the words or phrases in the box below. You can use the word or phrases once, more than once or not at all.

all completely different	two	clones	exactly the same	one

For an organism to reproduce asexually, *one* parent is needed. The offspring produced by this type of reproduction have genes which are *exactly the same* as the parent. They are said to be *clones* of each other.

Section Five — Genetics and Evolution

Questions on Sexual Reproduction

Q1 a) Complete the following sentences about sexual reproduction by circling the correct word in each of the brackets.

Sex cells are called ((gametes) / genes).

Male sex cells are called (testes / (sperm)). Female sex cells are called ((ova) / ovaries).

When sex cells join together this is called (pollination / (fertilisation)). The chromosomes ((pair up) / divide in two) and a (foetus / (zygote)) is formed.

b) Complete the diagram below to show what the chromosomes are like in the fertilised egg.

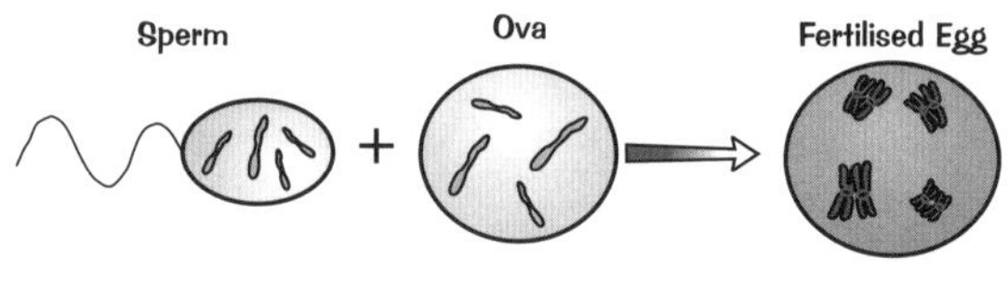

Sperm   Ova   Fertilised Egg

c) Do you think that in this form of reproduction, genetic information is inherited from one parent or both parents? *Both parents*

d) Complete the following sentence by circling the correct word in the brackets:
Offspring produced by sexual reproduction are genetically (identical / (different)) to their parents.

Q2 In the diagrams below, ⟞● represents a sperm, ◯ represents an egg, and ● the zygote.

A   B   C   D

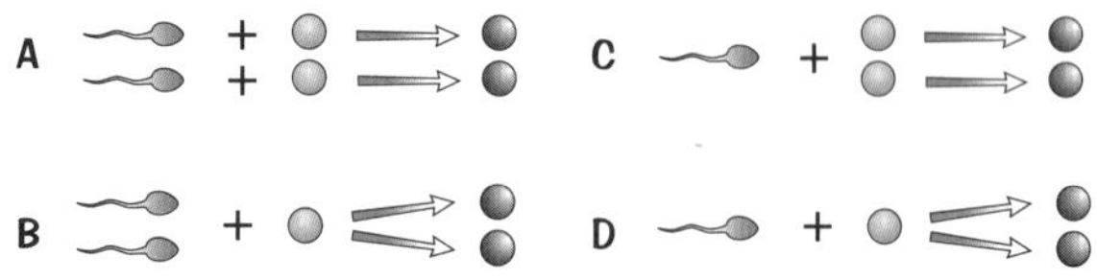

a) Which of the diagrams shows how identical twins can be formed? Diagram *D*

b) Which of the diagrams shows how non-identical twins can be formed? Diagram *A*

Section Five — Genetics and Evolution

Questions on Reproduction in Humans

Q1 The charts below show what happens in the menstrual cycle when a woman does not become pregnant.

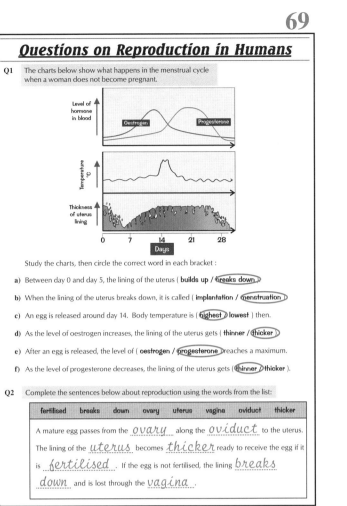

Study the charts, then circle the correct word in each bracket :

a) Between day 0 and day 5, the lining of the uterus (builds up / (breaks down))

b) When the lining of the uterus breaks down, it is called (implantation / (menstruation))

c) An egg is released around day 14. Body temperature is ((highest) / lowest) then.

d) As the level of oestrogen increases, the lining of the uterus gets (thinner / (thicker))

e) After an egg is released, the level of (oestrogen / (progesterone)) reaches a maximum.

f) As the level of progesterone decreases, the lining of the uterus gets ((thinner) / thicker).

Q2 Complete the sentences below about reproduction using the words from the list:

fertilised	breaks	down	ovary	uterus	vagina	oviduct	thicker

A mature egg passes from the *ovary* along the *oviduct* to the uterus.

The lining of the *uterus* becomes *thicker* ready to receive the egg if it

is *fertilised* . If the egg is not fertilised, the lining *breaks*

down and is lost through the *vagina* .

Section Five — Genetics and Evolution

Questions on Inheritance

Q1 a) Put a tick ✓ in the box ☐ next to each correct sentence about inheritance of sex (gender):

☑ Males have one X chromosome and one Y chromosome.

☑ Females have two X chromosomes.

☑ A sperm can contain an X chromosome or a Y chromosome.

☐ An egg can contain only a Y chromosome.

b) The sentence without a tick is incorrect.
Write down a correct version of it in the space below.
An egg can contain only an X chromosome

Q2 The diagram below shows some of the events leading to the production of a baby.

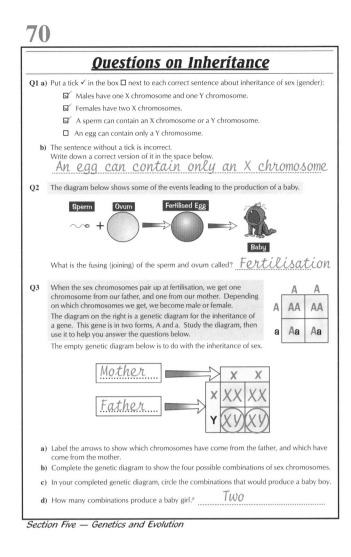

What is the fusing (joining) of the sperm and ovum called? *Fertilisation*

Q3 When the sex chromosomes pair up at fertilisation, we get one chromosome from our father, and one from our mother. Depending on which chromosomes we get, we become male or female.
The diagram on the right is a genetic diagram for the inheritance of a gene. This gene is in two forms, A and a. Study the diagram, then use it to help you answer the questions below.

	A	A
A	AA	AA
a	Aa	Aa

The empty genetic diagram below is to do with the inheritance of sex.

Mother →

	X	X
X	XX	XX
Y	(XY)	(XY)

Father →

a) Label the arrows to show which chromosomes have come from the father, and which have come from the mother.

b) Complete the genetic diagram to show the four possible combinations of sex chromosomes.

c) In your completed genetic diagram, circle the combinations that would produce a baby boy.

d) How many combinations produce a baby girl? *Two*

Section Five — Genetics and Evolution

Questions on Inheritance

Q4 a) Fill in the boxes to complete the genetic diagram below showing the inheritance of sex:

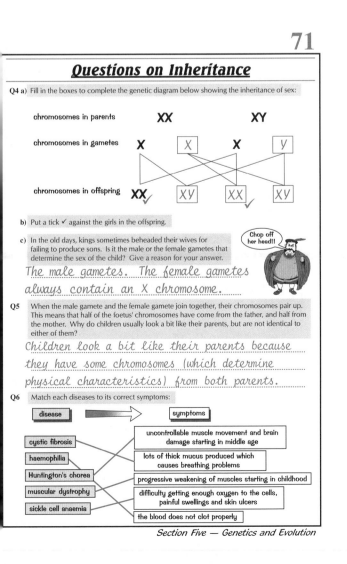

chromosomes in parents   **XX**   **XY**

chromosomes in gametes   **X** [X] **X** [Y]

chromosomes in offspring **XX** ✓ [XY] [XX] ✓ [XY]

b) Put a tick ✓ against the girls in the offspring.

c) In the old days, kings sometimes beheaded their wives for failing to produce sons. Is it the male or the female gametes that determine the sex of the child? Give a reason for your answer.

The male gametes. The female gametes always contain an X chromosome.

Q5 When the male gamete and the female gamete join together, their chromosomes pair up. This means that half of the foetus' chromosomes have come from the father, and half from the mother. Why do children usually look a bit like their parents, but are not identical to either of them?

Children look a bit like their parents because they have some chromosomes (which determine physical characteristics) from both parents.

Q6 Match each diseases to its correct symptoms:

disease →→→ symptoms

- cystic fibrosis
- haemophilia
- Huntington's chorea
- muscular dystrophy
- sickle cell anaemia

- uncontrollable muscle movement and brain damage starting in middle age
- lots of thick mucus produced which causes breathing problems
- progressive weakening of muscles starting in childhood
- difficulty getting enough oxygen to the cells, painful swellings and skin ulcers
- the blood does not clot properly

Section Five — Genetics and Evolution

Questions on Inheritance

Q7 Sickle cell anaemia is a disorder of the red blood cells. It must be inherited from both parents. The parents need not have the disease. They can still pass it on without having it themselves if they are both carriers of the disease.

a) What is a carrier? *Someone who has the gene but is not a sufferer*

b) Why can being a carrier of the disorder be an advantage in countries where there's a lot of malaria?
Carriers of sickle cell anaemia are immune to malaria.

Q8 a) Complete the following paragraph about Cystic fibrosis

chest	mucus	genetic	defective	digestive	both

Cystic fibrosis is a *genetic* disease. One in twenty people in this country

carry the *defective* gene. A person will only develop cystic fibrosis if

they inherit the gene from *both* of their parents. Parents are often

carriers of the disorder without developing cystic fibrosis themselves. Sufferers'

membranes produce thick sticky *mucus* in the lungs and pancreas causing

chest infections and *digestive* problems.

b) How could you inherit the disease from parents who do not have the disease themselves?
If both parents are carriers.

Q9 a) Complete the following paragraph about Huntington's Chorea

mental	disease	worse	nervous	one

Huntington's Chorea is a disorder of the *nervous* system. It can be inherited

from just *one* parent who has the disorder. Symptoms only develop when the

person who has inherited the disorder is over 35-40 years of age. The *disease*

causes involuntary movements and *mental* deterioration. There is no cure

and the condition gets progressively *worse* .

b) How is it possible that a young person has Huntington's Chorea without realising it?
The symptoms don't appear until later in life.

Section Five — Genetics and Evolution

Questions on Selective Breeding

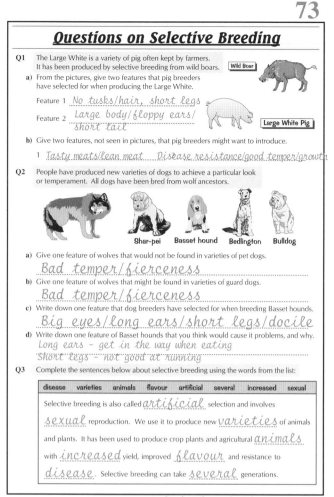

Q1 The Large White is a variety of pig often kept by farmers. It has been produced by selective breeding from wild boars.

  a) From the pictures, give two features that pig breeders have selected for when producing the Large White.

  Feature 1 _No tusks/hair, short legs_

  Feature 2 _Large body/floppy ears/ short tail_

  b) Give two features, not seen in pictures, that pig breeders might want to introduce.

  1 _Tasty meats/lean meat   Disease resistance/good temper/growth_

Q2 People have produced new varieties of dogs to achieve a particular look or temperament. All dogs have been bred from wolf ancestors.

Shar-pei   Basset hound   Bedlington   Bulldog

  a) Give one feature of wolves that would not be found in varieties of pet dogs.
  Bad temper/fierceness

  b) Give one feature of wolves that might be found in varieties of guard dogs.
  Bad temper/fierceness

  c) Write down one feature that dog breeders have selected for when breeding Basset hounds.
  Big eyes/long ears/short legs/docile

  d) Write down one feature of Basset hounds that you think would cause it problems, and why.
  Long ears - get in the way when eating   Short legs - not good at running

Q3 Complete the sentences below about selective breeding using the words from the list:

disease	varieties	animals	flavour	artificial	several	increased	sexual

Selective breeding is also called _artificial_ selection and involves _sexual_ reproduction. We use it to produce new _varieties_ of animals and plants. It has been used to produce crop plants and agricultural _animals_ with _increased_ yield, improved _flavour_ and resistance to _disease_. Selective breeding can take _several_ generations.

Section Five — Genetics and Evolution

Questions on Mutations

Q1 Genes can change into new forms. These new forms of genes are called mutations.

  a) What is a mutation? _A MUTATION is a change in a gene, which leads to genetic variation._

  b) Put a tick ✓ in the box ☐ next to each correct sentence about mutations:
  ☐ Infra-red light can increase the chance of mutations occurring.
  ☑ X-rays can increase the chance of mutations occurring.
  ☑ Gamma radiation from radioactive substances can increase the chance of mutations.
  ☑ Chemicals called mutagens can increase the chance of mutations occurring.

  c) The sentence without a tick is incorrect. Write down a correct version of it in the space below. _Ultra-violet light can increase the chances of mutations occurring_
  OR _Infra-red light can't increase the chance of mutations occurring._

Q2 Mutations can be a chemical change in just one gene, or they can be a major change in one or more chromosomes. The diagram on the right shows part of two fruit flies, and the chromosomes in a cell from each.

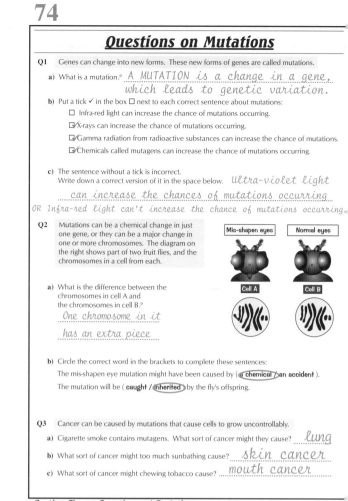

  a) What is the difference between the chromosomes in cell A and the chromosomes in cell B? _One chromosome in it has an extra piece_

  b) Circle the correct word in the brackets to complete these sentences:
  The mis-shapen eye mutation might have been caused by (**a chemical**/ an accident).
  The mutation will be (caught /**inherited**) by the fly's offspring.

Q3 Cancer can be caused by mutations that cause cells to grow uncontrollably.

  a) Cigarette smoke contains mutagens. What sort of cancer might they cause? _lung_

  b) What sort of cancer might too much sunbathing cause? _skin cancer_

  c) What sort of cancer might chewing tobacco cause? _mouth cancer_

Section Five — Genetics and Evolution

Questions on Mutations

Q4 Down's Syndrome is a genetic disease caused by a fault in the way the chromosomes separate when the mother's gametes are being formed. People with Down's Syndrome can live very fulfilled lives, but suffer from learning difficulties and a shortened life-span.

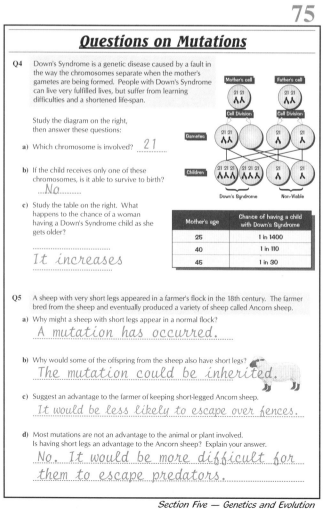

Study the diagram on the right, then answer these questions:

  a) Which chromosome is involved? _21_

  b) If the child receives only one of these chromosomes, is it able to survive to birth? _No_

  c) Study the table on the right. What happens to the chance of a woman having a Down's Syndrome child as she gets older?

  It increases

Mother's age	Chance of having a child with a Down's Syndrome
25	1 in 1400
40	1 in 110
45	1 in 30

Q5 A sheep with very short legs appeared in a farmer's flock in the 18th century. The farmer bred from the sheep and eventually produced a variety of sheep called Ancorn sheep.

  a) Why might a sheep with short legs appear in a normal flock?
  A mutation has occurred.

  b) Why would some of the offspring from the sheep also have short legs?
  The mutation could be inherited.

  c) Suggest an advantage to the farmer of keeping short-legged Ancorn sheep.
  It would be less likely to escape over fences.

  d) Most mutations are not an advantage to the animal or plant involved. Is having short legs an advantage to the Ancorn sheep? Explain your answer.
  No. It would be more difficult for them to escape predators.

Section Five — Genetics and Evolution

Questions on Fossils and Evolution

Q1 Fossils are the remains of animals and plants that died many years ago. Normally when organisms die, they decay. If the conditions needed for decay are not there, they may be fossilised.

Olenellus (trilobite)

The pictures below show three types of fossils. Peat Bog Man was preserved because there was little oxygen in the water-logged peat, and the acidic conditions made it difficult for decay bacteria to grow.

Draw lines to match the insect and the mammoth to the missing conditions for decay.

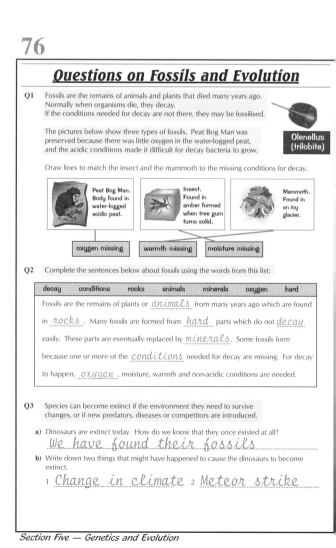

oxygen missing   warmth missing   moisture missing

Q2 Complete the sentences below about fossils using the words from this list:

decay	conditions	rocks	animals	minerals	oxygen	hard

Fossils are the remains of plants or _animals_ from many years ago which are found in _rocks_. Many fossils are formed from _hard_ parts which do not _decay_ easily. These parts are eventually replaced by _minerals_. Some fossils form because one or more of the _conditions_ needed for decay are missing. For decay to happen, _oxygen_, moisture, warmth and non-acidic conditions are needed.

Q3 Species can become extinct if the environment they need to survive changes, or if new predators, diseases or competitors are introduced.

  a) Dinosaurs are extinct today. How do we know that they once existed at all?
  We have found their fossils

  b) Write down two things that might have happened to cause the dinosaurs to become extinct.
  1 _Change in climate_ 2 _Meteor strike_

Section Five — Genetics and Evolution

Questions on Fossils and Evolution

Q4 Life on Earth is thought to be very old, with the first simple living things developing more than three billion years ago. The theory of evolution says that all the species of organisms alive today, and others that are now extinct, evolved from other simpler organisms.

The horse evolved to its modern appearance over millions of years. Study the diagram on the right, then answer the questions below.

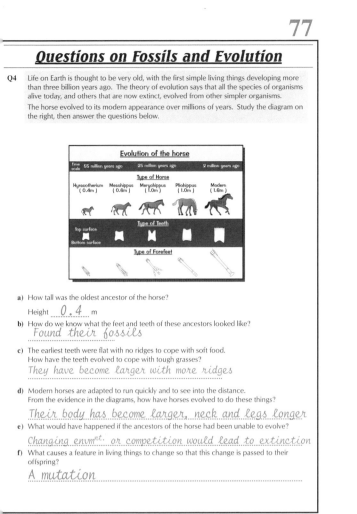

a) How tall was the oldest ancestor of the horse?

Height *0.4* m

b) How do we know what the feet and teeth of these ancestors looked like?

Found their fossils

c) The earliest teeth were flat with no ridges to cope with soft food. How have the teeth evolved to cope with tough grasses?

They have become larger with more ridges

d) Modern horses are adapted to run quickly and to see into the distance. From the evidence in the diagrams, how have horses evolved to do these things?

Their body has become larger, neck and legs longer

e) What would have happened if the ancestors of the horse had been unable to evolve?

Changing envmnt· or competition would lead to extinction

f) What causes a feature in living things to change so that this change is passed to their offspring?

A mutation

Section Five — Genetics and Evolution

Questions on Population Sizes

Q1 *The chart on the right shows the change in the numbers of a species of predator and its prey.*

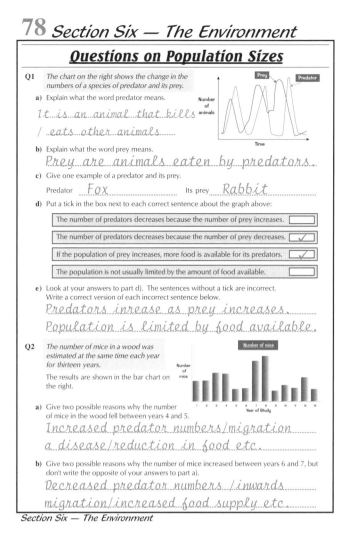

a) Explain what the word predator means.

It is an animal that kills / eats other animals

b) Explain what the word prey means.

Prey are animals eaten by predators·

c) Give one example of a predator and its prey.

Predator *Fox*   Its prey *Rabbit*

d) Put a tick in the box next to each correct sentence about the graph above:

The number of predators decreases because the number of prey increases.	
The number of predators decreases because the number of prey decreases.	✓
If the population of prey increases, more food is available for its predators.	✓
The population is not usually limited by the amount of food available.	

e) Look at your answers to part d). The sentences without a tick are incorrect. Write a correct version of each incorrect sentence below.

Predators inrease as prey increases·
Population is limited by food available·

Q2 *The number of mice in a wood was estimated at the same time each year for thirteen years.*

The results are shown in the bar chart on the right.

a) Give two possible reasons why the number of mice in the wood fell between years 4 and 5.

Increased predator numbers/migration a disease/reduction in food etc·

b) Give two possible reasons why the number of mice increased between years 6 and 7, but don't write the opposite of your answers to part a).

Decreased predator numbers /inwards migration/increased food supply etc·

Section Six — The Environment

Questions on Populations

Q1 *The graph below shows the average daytime temperature (line) and rainfall (bars) on the northern edge of the Sahara desert.*

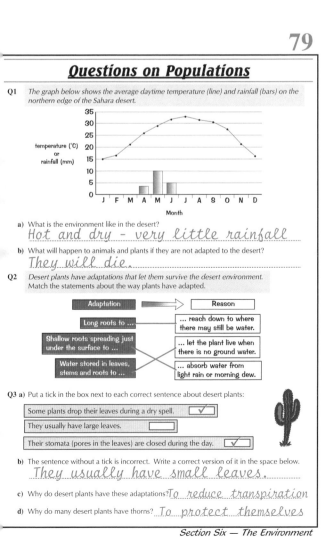

a) What is the environment like in the desert?

Hot and dry - very little rainfall

b) What will happen to animals and plants if they are not adapted to the desert?

They will die·

Q2 Desert plants have adaptations that let them survive the desert environment. Match the statements about the way plants have adapted.

Adaptation	→	Reason
Long roots to ...		... reach down to where there may still be water.
Shallow roots spreading just under the surface to ...		... let the plant live when there is no ground water.
Water stored in leaves, stems and roots to ...		... absorb water from light rain or morning dew.

Q3 a) Put a tick in the box next to each correct sentence about desert plants:

Some plants drop their leaves during a dry spell.	✓
They usually have large leaves.	
Their stomata (pores in the leaves) are closed during the day.	✓

b) The sentence without a tick is incorrect. Write a correct version of it in the space below.

They usually have small leaves·

c) Why do desert plants have these adaptations? *To reduce transpiration*

d) Why do many desert plants have thorns? *To protect themselves*

Section Six — The Environment

Questions on Populations

Q4 *The sidewinder adder lives in deserts. It moves sideways across the sand by throwing its body into a series of S-shapes, always keeping a loop off the ground, with two other parts touching.*

Why does it do this?

To keep itself cool by not having its whole body in contact with land.

Q5 *Many desert animals, such as the kangaroo rat, spend the day in a burrow and come out only at night.*

a) Write down two advantages of doing this.

Advantage 1 *It is cooler at night/conserve moisture*

Advantage 2 *Keep hidden from predators*

b) Write down a disadvantage of doing this.

Difficult to find food in the dark.

Q6 *Camels are probably the best-known animals in the desert.*

a) Describe the features that the camels have which make them adapted for desert conditions.

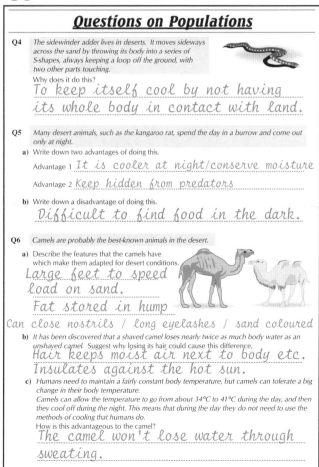

Large feet to speed load on sand.
Fat stored in hump
Can close nostrils / long eyelashes / sand coloured

b) *It has been discovered that a shaved camel loses nearly twice as much body water as an unshaved camel.* Suggest why losing its hair could cause this difference.

Hair keeps moist air next to body etc.
Insulates against the hot sun.

c) *Humans need to maintain a fairly constant body temperature, but camels can tolerate a big change in their body temperature.*
Camels can allow the temperature to go from about 34°C to 41°C during the day, and then they cool off during the night. This means that during the day they do not need to use the methods of cooling that humans do.
How is this advantageous to the camel?

The camel won't lose water through sweating.

Section Six — The Environment

Questions on Populations

Q7 *The graph below shows the average daytime temperature (line) and rainfall (bars) in the Arctic.*

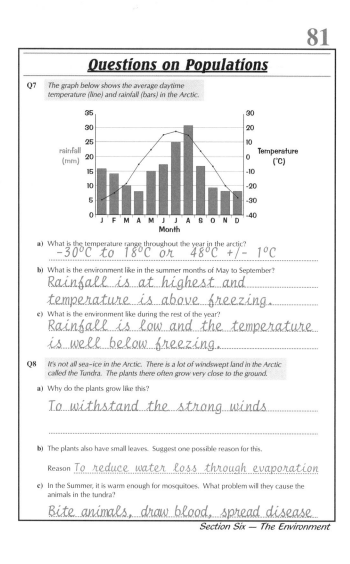

a) What is the temperature range throughout the year in the arctic?

-30°C to 18°C or 48°C +/- 1°C

b) What is the environment like in the summer months of May to September?

Rainfall is at highest and temperature is above freezing.

c) What is the environment like during the rest of the year?

Rainfall is low and the temperature is well below freezing.

Q8 *It's not all sea-ice in the Arctic. There is a lot of windswept land in the Arctic called the Tundra. The plants there often grow very close to the ground.*

a) Why do the plants grow like this?

To withstand the strong winds

b) The plants also have small leaves. Suggest one possible reason for this.

Reason *To reduce water loss through evaporation*

c) In the Summer, it is warm enough for mosquitoes. What problem will they cause the animals in the tundra?

Bite animals, draw blood, spread disease

Section Six — The Environment

Questions on Populations

Q9 *Large animals have a small surface area to volume ratio. This means that they lose heat more slowly than animals with a large surface area to volume ratio.*

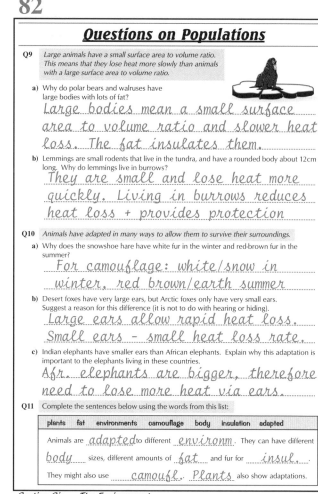

a) Why do polar bears and walruses have large bodies with lots of fat?

Large bodies mean a small surface area to volume ratio and slower heat loss. The fat insulates them.

b) Lemmings are small rodents that live in the tundra, and have a rounded body about 12cm long. Why do lemmings live in burrows?

They are small and lose heat more quickly. Living in burrows reduces heat loss + provides protection

Q10 *Animals have adapted in many ways to allow them to survive their surroundings.*

a) Why does the snowshoe hare have white fur in the winter and red-brown fur in the summer?

For camouflage: white/snow in winter, red brown/earth summer

b) Desert foxes have very large ears, but Arctic foxes only have very small ears. Suggest a reason for this difference (it is not to do with hearing or hiding).

Large ears allow rapid heat loss. Small ears - small heat loss rate.

c) Indian elephants have smaller ears than African elephants. Explain why this adaptation is important to the elephants living in these countries.

Afr. elephants are bigger, therefore need to lose more heat via ears.

Q11 Complete the sentences below using the words from this list:

plants	fat	environments	camouflage	body	insulation	adapted

Animals are *adapted* to different *environm*. They can have different *body* sizes, different amounts of *fat* and fur for *insul*.
They might also use *camoufl*. *Plants* also show adaptations.

Section Six — The Environment

Questions on The Greenhouse Effect

Q1 *The temperature on the surface of the Moon ranges from -175°C to 125°C. The average temperature on the surface of the Moon is about -20°C.*

The differences between the Moon's surface temperature and the Earth's surface temperature are because the Earth has an atmosphere. Our atmosphere traps heat by a process known as the greenhouse effect.

Complete the diagram below to show how the greenhouse effect works.

Choose from these labels:

Earth's surface
Earth's atmosphere
Heat from the Sun
Heat absorbed by the atmosphere

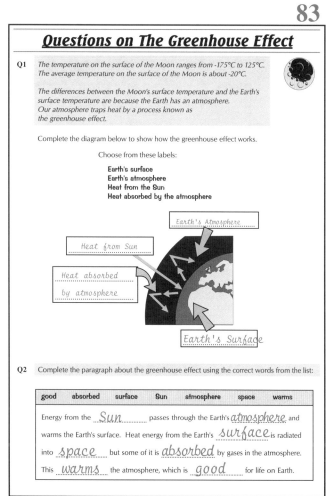

Q2 Complete the paragraph about the greenhouse effect using the correct words from the list:

good	absorbed	surface	Sun	atmosphere	space	warms

Energy from the *Sun* passes through the Earth's *atmosphere* and warms the Earth's surface. Heat energy from the Earth's *surface* is radiated into *space* but some of it is *absorbed* by gases in the atmosphere. This *warms* the atmosphere, which is *good* for life on Earth.

Section Six — The Environment

Questions on The Greenhouse Effect

Q3 *Look at the graphs below. They show the amount of carbon released from burning fossil fuels each year since 1850, and the percentage of carbon dioxide in the air each year since 1850.*

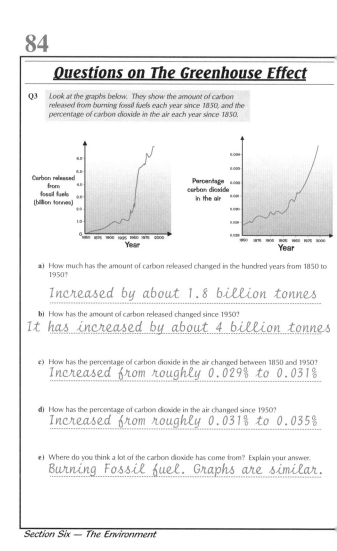

a) How much has the amount of carbon released changed in the hundred years from 1850 to 1950?

Increased by about 1.8 billion tonnes

b) How has the amount of carbon released changed since 1950?

It has increased by about 4 billion tonnes

c) How has the percentage of carbon dioxide in the air changed between 1850 and 1950?

Increased from roughly 0.029% to 0.031%

d) How has the percentage of carbon dioxide in the air changed since 1950?

Increased from roughly 0.031% to 0.035%

e) Where do you think a lot of the carbon dioxide has come from? Explain your answer.

Burning Fossil fuel. Graphs are similar.

Section Six — The Environment

Questions on The Greenhouse Effect

Q4 *The graphs below show the changes in average temperatures and sea level since 1880.*

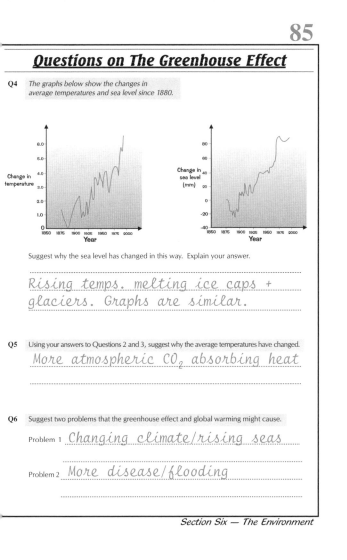

Suggest why the sea level has changed in this way. Explain your answer.

Rising temps. melting ice caps + glaciers. Graphs are similar.

Q5 Using your answers to Questions 2 and 3, suggest why the average temperatures have changed.

More atmospheric CO_2 absorbing heat

Q6 Suggest two problems that the greenhouse effect and global warming might cause.

Problem 1 *Changing climate/rising seas*

Problem 2 *More disease/flooding*

Section Six — The Environment

Questions on Acid Rain

Q1 *The table below shows the amount of acid rain gases from different sources.*

The percentage contributions of nitrogen oxides have been plotted on the graph below.

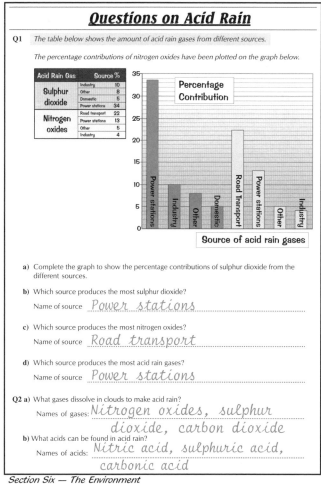

Acid Rain Gas	Source	%
Sulphur dioxide	Industry	10
	Other	8
	Domestic	5
	Power stations	34
Nitrogen oxides	Road transport	22
	Power stations	13
	Other	5
	Industry	4

a) Complete the graph to show the percentage contributions of sulphur dioxide from the different sources.

b) Which source produces the most sulphur dioxide?

Name of source *Power stations*

c) Which source produces the most nitrogen oxides?

Name of source *Road transport*

d) Which source produces the most acid rain gases?

Name of source *Power stations*

Q2 a) What gases dissolve in clouds to make acid rain?

Names of gases: *Nitrogen oxides, sulphur dioxide, carbon dioxide*

b) What acids can be found in acid rain?

Names of acids: *Nitric acid, sulphuric acid, carbonic acid*

Section Six — The Environment

Questions on Farming and its Problems

Q1 Look at this food chain, then answer the questions:

rose bush ⟹ greenfly ⟹ ladybird ⟹ great tit

a) Circle the correct answer from each of the underlined pairs:

Insecticide will kill the rose bush / ~~greenfly~~.

Ladybirds eat great tits / ~~greenfly~~.

If there are fewer greenfly, there will be more / ~~less food~~ for the great tits.

b) Look at your answers to part a). Explain briefly what might happen to great tits if a gardener uses an insecticide spray to protect their rose bushes.

This kills greenflies, reducing food available to ladyb, less food for GT.

Q2 a) Put a tick in the box next to each correct sentence about *pesticides*:

Pesticides kill insects.	✓
If pesticides kill bees, more flowers will be pollinated.	
The use of pesticides provides more food for many birds.	

b) Look at the sentences without a tick. Write down the correct versions of the sentences.

If insecticides kill bees, fewer flowers pollinated.

Use of insecticides provides less food for many birds

Q3 Complete the sentences below using the words from the list:

fish fertilisers insects minerals pollinating chains pesticides oxygen

Farmers use *pesticides* to kill *insects* and other pests that reduce crop yields. The use of these chemicals can disturb food *chains* and reduce the number of *pollinating* insects. Farmers use *fertilisers* to replace lost *minerals* in the soil, but they can cause the amount of *oxygen* in rivers to decrease, and so reduce the number of *fish* and other animals.

Section Six — The Environment

Questions on Pyramids of Numbers & Biomass

Q1 Look at this food chain: carrot → rabbit → fox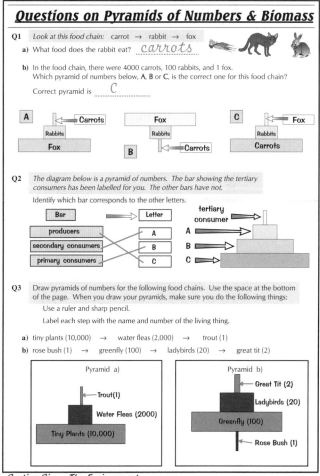

a) What food does the rabbit eat? *carrots*

b) In the food chain, there were 4000 carrots, 100 rabbits, and 1 fox. Which pyramid of numbers below, **A**, **B** or **C**, is the correct one for this food chain?

Correct pyramid is *C*

A Carrots / Rabbits / Fox

B Fox / Rabbits / Carrots

C Fox / Rabbits / Carrots

Q2 The diagram below is a pyramid of numbers. The bar showing the tertiary consumers has been labelled for you. The other bars have not.

Identify which bar corresponds to the other letters.

Bar	Letter
producers	A
secondary consumers	B
primary consumers	C

tertiary consumer → A, B, C

Q3 Draw pyramids of numbers for the following food chains. Use the space at the bottom of the page. When you draw your pyramids, make sure you do the following things:

Use a ruler and sharp pencil.

Label each step with the name and number of the living thing.

a) tiny plants (10,000) → water fleas (2,000) → trout (1)

b) rose bush (1) → greenfly (100) → ladybirds (20) → great tit (2)

Pyramid a) — Trout (1) / Water Fleas (2000) / Tiny Plants (10,000)

Pyramid b) — Great Tit (2) / Ladybirds (20) / Greenfly (100) / Rose Bush (1)

Section Six — The Environment

Questions on Pyramids of Numbers & Biomass

Q4 Read the following sentences about biomass and pyramids of biomass and put a tick in the boxes next to the correct sentences.

Biomass is the number of living things.	☐
Biomass is the mass of living material.	✓
Pyramids of biomass show the biomass at each stage in a food chain.	✓
Pyramids of biomass cannot be drawn to scale.	☐
The biomass decreases from the beginning to the end of a food chain.	✓

Q5 One of the food chains in the North Sea is:

tiny plants → tiny animals → mackerel → cod.

The biomass of each living thing is shown in the table.

organism	biomass in kg
cod	2
mackerel	10
tiny animals	80
tiny plants	100

Draw the pyramid of biomass for this food chain in the space below.
I suggest you use a scale of 1mm for each kg.

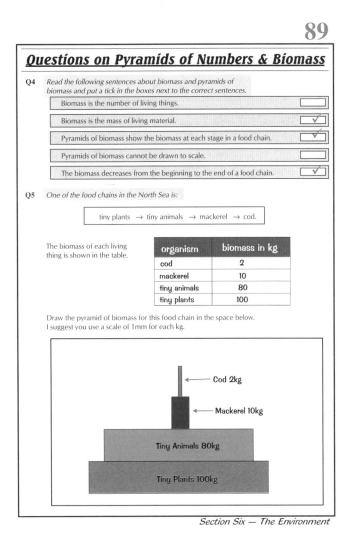

Cod 2kg
Mackerel 10kg
Tiny Animals 80kg
Tiny Plants 100kg

Section Six — The Environment

Questions on Pyramids of Numbers & Biomass

Q6 Look at the pyramid on the right.

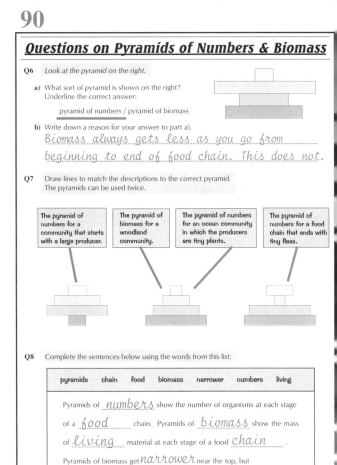

a) What sort of pyramid is shown on the right? Underline the correct answer:

<u>pyramid of numbers</u> / pyramid of biomass

b) Write down a reason for your answer to part a).

Biomass always gets less as you go from beginning to end of food chain. This does not.

Q7 Draw lines to match the descriptions to the correct pyramid. The pyramids can be used twice.

The pyramid of numbers for a community that starts with a large producer.	The pyramid of biomass for a woodland community.	The pyramid of numbers for an ocean community in which the producers are tiny plants.	The pyramid of numbers for a food chain that ends with tiny fleas.

Q8 Complete the sentences below using the words from this list:

pyramids   chain   food   biomass   narrower   numbers   living

Pyramids of *numbers* show the number of organisms at each stage of a *food* chain. Pyramids of *biomass* show the mass of *living* material at each stage of a food *chain*.

Pyramids of biomass get *narrower* near the top, but *pyramids* of number can be any shape.

Section Six — The Environment

Questions on The Carbon Cycle

Q1 There are two equations you need to know: one for photosynthesis and one for respiration.

a) Complete the word equation below for photosynthesis:

Carbon dioxide + *water* → glucose + *oxygen*

b) Complete the word equation below for respiration:

glucose + oxygen → water + *carbon dioxide*

Q2 The diagram below shows part of the carbon cycle. Use your answers to question 1 to fill in the missing words. Choose from the list below left (you will not need them all):

photosynthesis
respiration
oxygen
carbon dioxide
water
glucose

carbon dioxide
in the atmosphere

respiration   *photosynthesis*

Carbon Compounds
in plants

Q3 a) What gas, found in air, is needed for burning to happen? *oxygen*

b) Water vapour is produced when wood burns. What other gas is produced when wood burns? *carbon dioxide*

c) Complete the word equation for wood burning. Use your answers to parts a) and b) to help you.

wood + *oxygen* → *carbon dioxide* + *water*

Q4 Fill in the missing words in the sentences below. Choose from this list of words:

glucose   up   down   respiration   oxygen   photosynthesis   burn   carbon dioxide

Plants make glucose from *carbon dioxide* and water. This process is called *photosynth.*. It causes the amount of carbon dioxide in the air to go *down*. Animals, plants and bacteria produce energy from *glucose* using the process called *respiration*. This process causes the amount of carbon dioxide in the air to go *up*. When wood and other fuels *burn*, *oxygen* from the air is used up, and more carbon dioxide is produced.

Section Six — The Environment

Questions on The Carbon Cycle

Q5 Bacteria and fungi are decomposers. They can break down solid waste materials from animals. They can also break down materials in dead animals and plants. This breakdown is called decay.

a) What can decomposers do? *Decomposers can break down solid waste material from dead animals etc.*

b) What is decay? *Decay is the breakdown of material by decomposers.*

c) Name two types of living thing that can cause decay: *bacteria* and *fungi*

Q6 Complete these sentences about decay by microbes. Circle the correct word from each of the underlined pairs:

a) Microbes break down materials faster when they are cool /(warm,) and in (moist) / dry conditions.

b) Many microbes work better if there is more (oxygen) / nitrogen in their environment.

Q7 Match the statements below to show the effect the three processes have on the amount of carbon dioxide in the air.

photosynthesis causes	carbon dioxide in the air to increase
decay (decomposition) causes	
burning and respiration cause	carbon dioxide in the air to decrease

Q8 Look at the diagram of the carbon cycle below.

Fill in the missing words to complete the diagram. Choose from the list below (some words may not be needed, and some words might be needed more than once):

animals   plants   decay   burning   feeding   respiration   photosynthesis

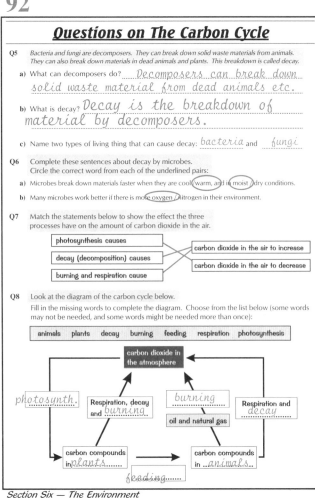

carbon dioxide in the atmosphere

photosynth.   Respiration, decay and *burning*   *burning*   Respiration and *decay*

oil and natural gas

carbon compounds in *plants*   carbon compounds in *animals*

feeding

Section Six — The Environment